G000275811

15 APR 1999

WITHDRAWN FROM
PLYMOUTH LIBRARY SERVICES

BOAT MAINTENANCE

Also by David Derrick
Navigation for Offshore and Ocean Sailors

BOAT MAINTENANCE

DAVID DERRICK

DAVID & CHARLES
Newton Abbot   London   North Pomfret (Vt)

British Library Cataloguing in Publication Data

Derrick, David
  Boat maintenance.
  1. Boats and boating – Maintenance and repair
  I. Title
  623.8′208   VM321

  ISBN 0-7153-8412-0

© David Derrick 1984

First published 1984
Second impression 1985
Third impression 1987

All rights reserved. No part of this
publication may be reproduced, stored in
a retrieval system, or transmitted, in
any form or by any means, electronic,
mechanical, photocopying, recording or
otherwise, without the prior permission
of David & Charles (Publishers) Limited

Typeset by Typesetters (Birmingham) Ltd
Edgbaston Road, Smethwick, Warley, West Midlands
and printed in Great Britain
by Redwood Burn Ltd, Trowbridge, Wilts
for David & Charles (Publishers) Ltd
Brunel House Newton Abbot Devon

Published in the United States of America
by David & Charles Inc
North Pomfret Vermont 05053 USA

ST. BUDEAUX

2 8 APR 1989

Contents

Acknowledgements

A book of this type is rarely the work of one person, and on this occasion the author is indebted to the following who, variously, gave advice, permitted photography on their premises or allowed staff to impart specialised knowledge: R. S. J. Barton Ltd, Blake & Sons (Gosport) Ltd, Blakes Paints Ltd, Burwin Marine Electronics Ltd, Ciba-Geigy Ltd, Devoncraft Ltd, Henderson Pumps & Equipment Ltd who also supplied the diagram on page 119, International Yacht Paints Ltd, Island Cruising Club, John McKillop & Co, Lewmar Marine Ltd who also supplied the photographs which appear on pages 94 and 95, Marlow Ropes Ltd, Salcombe Marine Ltd, Seafarer Navigation International Ltd, Simpson-Lawrence Ltd, South Western Marine Factors Ltd, Volvo Penta (UK) Ltd, Whisstocks Boatyard Ltd who also supplied the photographs on pages 52 and 72, Winter Boatyard Ltd, sundry friends from around the 'Island' in Salcombe and Tim Hall of David & Charles who has been very patient.

Finally, I am particularly grateful to my wife, Jennifer Johnson, who not only took some of the photographs and created all the line drawings, but also designed the book.

To all these I offer my sincere thanks for the communal support and apologise in advance for any mistakes I have not spotted which detract from the end product.

Introduction

I strongly believe that to have full confidence in a vessel, the owner or skipper should know every nook and cranny. From long experience of handling craft which were, initially at least, strange to me, I also know that the probing of those nooks and crannies, just for the sake of it, is not very exciting. How much nicer it is to find that intimate knowledge as an incidental to performing more practical, seamanlike tasks such as chipping rusty ballast and servicing heads.

In some ways, the employment of a yard to complete any work has a certain appeal, particularly if the bill is to be paid by someone else; in others, the true mariner must be tempted to do the work himself. Of necessity, the traditional sailor is a self-sufficient being. Though 'Self Sufficiency' and 'Do-it-Yourself' have become fashionable talking points and hobbies for some, the large group of small-boat sailors actually practise both. It is with these people in mind that this book has been written. Throughout, the object is to identify what needs doing, when to do it, how to do it and the tools and equipment which will be necessary. The true sailor is not easily led and it is the hope of the author that the offering of this collected information will be taken as advice. The reader will assess his own skill and circumstances and will thus know best when to leave the work to a yard. 'Do-it-Yourself' is both economical and satisfying. 'Doing it Again' is quite different.

The first three chapters can be taken as a starting point for the inexperienced or light reading for others. No two boats, no two people and no two voyages are alike, so any attempt at generalisation must bear that in mind. For example, when examining a hull for defects and damage, exactly what one can expect to find is greatly influenced by the material used for its construction and, to a lesser extent, the method of construction. In spite of the occasional magazine article indicating otherwise, so far as I am aware, there is no worm which eats glass-reinforced plastic, any more than an inflatable will rust or steel delaminate. The actual size of a boat has little bearing on the sort of problems from which it will suffer, so no direct reference is made to size, though it is assumed that the inflatable will be of the size and type normally used as a tender.

Rather than end up with a three-chapter book, all actual detail of maintenance and repairs have been considered in a separate context. Chapters 4–12 deal with a fairly broad subject and within their pages should be found the answers to most problems. The key to finding particular detail is in the index which appears at the end, though it is hoped that each of these chapters will be read as a way of collecting more ideas – surely a pastime we all enjoy.

1 Fitting Out

Each time you leave your home you 'equip' yourself in a manner suited to the daily tasks which you intend to perform. You 'fit out' for either office or squash, for rain or sun. The fitting out of a boat follows a similar principle, but with one very big difference. Unlike your day-to-day personal 'fit out', fitting out a boat will normally be executed just once for each season or in anticipation of a particular lengthy voyage. For this reason, it is not a task to be taken lightly, but one to be completed as meticulously as possible, with full regard paid to the type of sailing anticipated. Later, when the going gets rough, it is preferable to look back to this period with confidence borne from the knowledge of a job well done, rather than apprehension borne of a certain knowledge of numerous small, perhaps growing faults, the correction of which remain undone.

As long as the uncertainty of weather is with us, the fitting out of a boat will never follow a strict schedule. All that can be hoped for is a proposal for each working period which will allow for a choice between a task which needs specific weather and one which can be performed below decks or even at home.

High on the list of proposals should be one to gain access to the bottom. Not only will some of the work need good weather, but the correct timing of the tide might enable the work to be undertaken in daylight. Another consideration in the planning stage is that, come the spring, one or two other boat owners might be looking for a beach or wall to use. The booking of such facilities well in advance will often save disappointment and rushed, incomplete work.

Once the boat is dry, the bottom should be cleaned as thoroughly as possible. In fact, it can be advantageous to start cleaning before all the tidal water has gone away. The close proximity to the hull which cleaning demands also helps to start the next stage, a minute examination of every square inch for any sign of damage to the structure. Which particular damage will be at the forefront of your mind can only be determined by the structure of your boat. When examining the bottom for defects, it is worth considering the use of scaffolding or ladders to include the topsides. You will, of course, be paying extra attention to any areas of the hull suspected of leaking.

At the same time as inspecting the hull, it is possible to cast an eye over all the hull fittings. Every through-the-hull fitting needs examination. Seacocks will always have a flange mounted around the orifice on the outside of the hull, and the complete fitting, flange and all, will be fastened through the hull. If there is any suspicion of electrolytic or galvanic action, samples of the fastenings should be withdrawn to assess its extent. The first indication of such action will be the fastenings themselves looking discoloured or wasted. If the hull is of wood, the area around the fastening will also be discoloured.

If an echo-sounder transducer is fitted to the outside of the hull it will need to be treated gently. Its face is relatively fragile and if it is necessary to remove barnacles from it, crush them first with a pair of pliers. To simply pull them off might actually destroy the transducer. While on this subject, it is worth mentioning that if the boat is to be dried out reasonably often during the season, it will not be necessary to apply antifoul paint to the transducer. In fact, with most paints, the effect would be to reduce the capability of the instrument. If drying out is not envisaged, apply one thin coat of hard antifoul paint.

The propeller deserves a lot of attention. Evidence of electrolytic or galvanic action will be found on the leading edges of the blades, which will become thinner and thinner until eventually they are actually perforated. The fixing nuts should be tight and secured by either tab washers or, preferably, wire passing through both nuts and studs. By attempting to lift the boss of the propeller, the amount of slack between the propeller shaft and its bearings can be assessed. There is usually just enough slack to allow the movement to be felt. The outer end of the propeller shaft bearings might be of tufnol and lubricated with water, in which case, the tubes through which the water passes on its way to the bearing should be cleaned with a suitably thin screwdriver.

Give the rudder a shake to assess the wear in its hangings and.examine them to ensure that they are still securely attached to the hull and also that there is no sign of corrosion.

Somewhere on the hull will be a sacrificial anode or two, either in the form of a block or a collar around the shaft. If these blocks are connected to each and every skin fitting with a substantial gauge of copper wire on the inside of the hull, it is possible that they will look a little the worse for wear. If that is the case, renew them and be thankful that such a relatively cheap and easily replaced item has corroded rather than one of the expensive alternatives. If the anodes show no sign of wear, check the internal wiring.

A final check before embarking on any repairs and painting below the water line is to ensure that if fitted, the radio earth is securely fitted and connected. Usually only used with MF radios, these earths commonly take the form of a copper plate or a much smaller block, the surface of which is pimpled with numerous hemispheres covered with a suitable conductor.

Before finally leaving the wall or beach, all the seacocks will need servicing and all pipe fittings to skin fittings should also be closely examined.

Short of unforeseen disasters, the remaining work can be completed with the boat afloat. One of the early jobs to schedule, if not to perform, is a trip or two up the mast. To do so at ease and in safety, one mast-head halyard, at least, must be sound. The upper terminals, splices, tangs and shackles of each of the parts of the standing rigging must be examined for corrosion and security

and care taken that all split pins are working as intended and every shackle is wired. The mast-head sheaves ought to be dismantled, greased and reassembled, then the new running rigging installed. All electric wiring, including radio aerial leads, should be checked for both technical performance and security.

On deck, the lower ends of the standing rigging will need similar attention to that afforded the upper, before adjusting it. Then the bottle screws and shackles will be wired prior to oiling the galvanised wire.

Having serviced the winches, it will be time to give some attention to the sails. This will just confirm that all is well. First oil all the piston hanks, then run each up and down, checking for ease of operation the leads of sheets and the state of whippings and servings. When the main sail is set, check the reefing. If of the roller type, the gear will probably need lubricating. For slab reefing, ensure that all the various lines are available and easily identifiable and that the jamming cleats work.

The anchor and all its cable will be dragged on to deck so that it can be inspected thoroughly and, while it is there, the chain locker can be cleaned and painted. Check also the kedge and other anchors and all warps and fenders.

Install the emergency steering gear and make sure it is complete, then all that remains is to make sure that everything will move that ought to move. That entails wandering around armed with oil and grease checking things like hinges and ventilators.

One of the high-priority below-deck jobs must be that of checking the safety equipment. It is while engaged in activities like fitting out that accidents are more likely to happen and, in the event of a fire, even the presence of a liferaft might be appreciated. Presumably one bilge pump, at least, will have been serviceable for as long as the boat has been afloat. Now is the time to overhaul each individually, ensuring not only that it works, but that spares are available to keep it so.

With full safety equipment available, including a selection of bilge pumps, you will probably have enough confidence to turn your hand to more social tasks such as servicing the heads and fresh-water system. Other domestic tasks will include checking the cooker and airing the bedding.

If it has not already been done by this stage, the engine will need removing from its winter 'cocoon'. In addition to checking its waters, oils and belts, this is the best time to repack the stern gland, should that prove necessary. When the engine is running, the charging should be confirmed to be working as well, then all the electrics can be checked.

When all maintenance work, particularly engineering type, has been completed, the time will be right to clean out the bilges and paint them if required. If there is any internal ballast, that too should be cleaned and painted. When refitting ballast, make sure it is secure and is not likely to move in sympathy with the boat.

Time spent planning the period of fitting out is often rewarded with less 'undoing' of work performed earlier. It is inevitable that some faults will come to light only as the work 'progresses', but, generally speaking, if it is planned to effect the work in the order of repairing, cleaning and finally painting, there will be less likelihood of the necessity to repeat work. But do try to complete all the repairs before doing any of the painting. Yours would not be the first occasion on which new varnish work has been damaged by moving the heads or a cooker.

2 In Commission

While in commission, most maintenance will be occasioned by wear and tear, and that will come to light either when it happens or by regular, methodical inspection. A sheet which parts while its associated sail is in use is hardly an incident which will pass unnoticed, but dirt in a fuel system can get progressively worse and if unchecked will eventually cause the engine to stop 'just when you least expected it'.

A good skipper will frequently take a turn around deck just to make sure everything is as it should be. When sailing overnight, such a jaunt at first light often reveals a rigging fault or perhaps an anchor about to break loose. Presumably, in the dark, most of us are either incapable or unwilling to make a proper inspection.

Apart from anchors breaking free, a casual inspection might reveal a sheet gently rubbing against a shroud or an electric cable; it might be paint work which is being chafed or it might be a piston hank or a sail slide parting company from its parent sail. Whatever the fault, the quicker it is rectified, the greater the rewards. Those 'rewards' are, in fact, negative, since you will have less work in the long run.

Whenever sails are handled, it should become second nature to check stitching and seams and whether or not the piston hanks need oiling. Check to see whether the snap shackles are becoming stiff.

When considering the efficiency, or lack of it, of mechanical equipment, the view of a stranger is often worth more consideration than that of someone who, over a period of time, has been continuously adjusting the amount of effort required to overcome the gradually diminishing efficiency.

Most deck equipment, including sails, warps and fenders, will be in use sufficiently often to preclude the need for any other regular inspection. Less well used items such as reefing gear and kedge warps ought to appear on one check list or another.

At some time each day, preferably earlier rather than later so that any work resulting can be completed in daylight, the following will need to be checked. Some inspections will become incidental to other tasks, while some will require a specific effort.

The engine and all its associated equipment, that is the oil levels in the engine itself, the reduction box and the gearbox should be checked. The stern gland greaser should be turned up tightly. The cooling water level should be checked and the state of the sea-water strainer ascertained. If it is not to be used for its intended purpose of propelling the boat, run it up for long enough for it to attain its normal working temperature. Check the level of fuel in the tank and the state of fuel in the water traps.

Before pumping the bilge, lift a sole board. Apart from mucky water, there might be floating rubbish which is better removed by hand than by pump. The level and colour of the water might also contain a message. When pumping the bilge, share the load between all the available pumps. If any leak appears rectify it.

The levels of gas and fresh water should also be checked daily. Again, there might be a message concerning a leak implied in a

lower level than was expected. The heads will benefit not only from a daily clean, but from a flush through with soapy washing-up water.

At some time during each week, the checks should be increased to include the following. If taken in small steps, and executed when convenient, the chores are not only less arduous, but can be actually enjoyable.

Starting with the mechanics, the stern gland greaser will almost certainly need refilling with an appropriate grease. Clean the engine itself. Once clean, any leaks, whether they be of oil or water, are easily spotted and it will not require much effort to keep it so. All belts should be checked for tension and electrical connections for security. All the hose clips will need checking both for security and leaks. The batteries will need the electrolyte level checked and its specific gravity measured to ensure that the state of charge of the battery is satisfactory. Clean the battery.

All the safety equipment which has not been used in the previous week should be ascertained as serviceable and ready for instant use. This will normally include the liferaft, fire-fighting equipment and the pyrotechnics.

By dinghy if necessary, but from a marina pontoon should the opportunity present itself during the week, wash down the top-sides. If they are painted, cover any bare hull material for protection alone, even if for any reason a proper touching-in job cannot be done. If of GRP, repair any abrasions. Any deck paint or varnish work should also be made complete.

If the storm sails have not been in use recently, give them an airing while ascertaining their fitness for such a specific task. Lubricate the roller reefing gear and make sure that all the lines necessary to work the slab reefing are not only on board, but still long enough.

Yet another category of checks is that known as occasional. In its literal sense, this can be taken to mean as required. In other words, occasionally might be more often than weekly.

The stowage of gas bottles should be secure and that is something which can be checked each time a bottle is changed. At that time, what can also be checked without much effort is that the drain from the gas bottle locker is not blocked. Another check worth making after changing a bottle is for a leak. A squirt of washing-up liquid or soapy water around the neck of the bottle will soon reveal escaping gas.

Lifejackets, or at least those which have not been inflated recently, ought to be checked and safety harnesses will probably need a little oil on the snap hooks.

3 Laying Up

The laying up of a boat is, really, the first step of fitting out. The task of fitting out can be made so much easier by thoughtful and constructive laying up. The first major decision about laying up, whether it be for the winter or any other prolonged period, is whether it is to be afloat, ashore or in a mud berth.

If the boat is to be laid up on a swinging mooring in a tidal estuary and left unattended for long periods, the strength of the mooring must be assured. In most harbours and estuaries a shortage of yachting movement during the winter might mean the availability of a mooring larger than that which would normally be allocated. Use a length of substantial chain to attach the boat to the mooring, attaching it to the riser beneath the buoy. A length of heavy-duty polythene pipe over the whole length of chain will help to protect the bow when the wind is blowing against the tide.

A fore-and-aft mooring is a little better, if only for the extra security of the second mooring. It is usually better to face the flood tide, the stronger of the two, which will often mean facing the strongest winds as well. Whichever type of mooring is used, if there is any danger of ice, it would be as well to lash a V of timber to the uptide mooring to break it up. Small amounts of ice can cause a surprisingly large amount of damage at the water line. If the expected amount of ice was more than a little, it would be unwise to lay up the boat there.

Provided the boat is happy to take the bottom without outside assistance, a mud berth can be excellent value for a winter period. The boat should be moored all fours, that is, with an anchor from each bow and one from each quarter. This will keep the boat in a more-or-less fixed position and allow her to dig herself a hollow into which she should comfortably settle at each low water. Mud berths often have an extra facility of allowing access to boat by means of a plank rather than by dinghy.

A final alternative is to have the boat craned or cradled on to a hard standing. In many ways this is the most satisfactory, since access is easy, as is usually the availability of water and electricity. Unfortunately, most of the craning and cradling is organised by boatyards which, for fairly obvious reasons, discourage owners from working on their boats.

If the boat is not to spend the laid-up period ashore or very close to it, the moving ashore of loads of gear might not be very easy. It might be worth preparing all the gear for disembarking, then making a temporary trip alongside a wall for one massive unloading. Such a trip can often be combined with a final inspection of the bottom.

It will be as well to take ashore all equipment which will suffer from being wet. This will include all soft furnishings, such as bedding, mattresses, pillows and cushions. Most of the electronic equipment can be removed easily and that will probably fare better in a loft than a damp old boat. Remember to remove all dry batteries from such gear. If there is room, the inflated lifejackets could be put in the loft as well, as could the safety harnesses. Though the pyrotechnics will be better stored somewhere dry, your fire insurance company might not approve of them being in the house.

Other items to go ashore are all the sails for inspection, repair and washing, the liferaft to be taken to an authorised repair agent and fire extinguishers if they are to be checked. If the engine is to be inhibited, having done so, the batteries should be taken ashore and given a charge once each month. When taking equipment ashore, do not get too carried away because you might need some left on board either for safety or convenience, depending on where the boat is laid up and the work you intend to undertake during the winter.

If the engine is of the petrol variety and it is decided not to inhibit it, the very least that can be done to ease the starting problem at fit out is to completely drain the fuel system. This means from the tank, pipes, filters and carburettor. Over a prolonged period the more volatile fractions of the fuel will evaporate and there is a good chance of that leaving a gummy deposit in all the wrong places. Of course, whatever the type of engine, it is better to inhibit it completely.

All the fresh water should be drained completely from all parts of the system. That might entail slacking off hose clips at some points to be absolutely certain of success.

Everything which might possibly need grease or oil should be offered it, including all hinges, doorlocks, padlocks, cooker taps and barrel bolts. Deck winches and the anchor windlass should be given a full service and lubrication.

Fancy work will need a particularly good polish and then a smear of petroleum jelly or clear varnish. The lockers ought to be emptied of the season's accumulation of rubbish, most of which can probably be thrown away, and then scrubbed clean.

If the mast has been unstepped, then all the rigging can be taken away for a leisurely inspection, otherwise it must be done on board. Most of the running rigging should be removed, leaving one or two mast head gantlines available for use in re-reaving the proper halyards during fit out. Some of the standing might be removed, but if any is, try to take some of the strain the removed piece was intended to take by an imaginative lead of a halyard or gantline. Any galvanised rigging must be cleaned with a wire brush and oiled if it cannot be taken to a protected environment for the winter. All the remaining rigging will need really good frapping – that means better than most of us appear to think of as adequate. Clanking halyards inevitably follow winter gales, which are often much stronger than those experienced in the summer, even though less people experience them.

All paint work should be made a complete surface, even, if absolutely necessary, by using a different coloured paint. For the winter, the protection is probably more important than the appearance. The bottom should also be examined for damage, but there is little point in adding antifoul paint lower than about 14in (350mm) below the water line. Weed will only attach itself to a part of the hull where light is available. Varnished wood should have all darkened

areas removed by rubbing down and at least one coat of diluted varnish and one full coat added. More coats would be even better, even though a lot of the extra varnish will be rubbed off during the next fit out.

The last, but by no means least, task is to arrange for adequate ventilation. Every door, including those for the lockers, should be securely lashed open. Most of the cabin sole boards should be raised to allow a circulation of air through the bilge. All the ventilators should be set to allow a maximum amount of air in and out for the minimum amount of water.

On deck, rig a fore-and-aft waterproof awning, preferably over a ridge pole, but if not over a warp stretched as tightly as possible. Hold the edges down with strong synthetic lines passing right under the boat.

A final safety precaution is to ask a local who spends a lot of time on the water to keep an eye on your boat.

4 Getting to the Bottom of It

The examination of the bottom of your boat, that is, the part of the hull which is normally under water, is essential for complete fitting out or laying up. Additionally, it will be necessary at any other time if below-water damage is suspected. Standing your boat on a beach or leaning it against a wall is also a useful way to extend your cruising grounds to include drying harbours.

In non-tidal waters access to the bottom of your boat can be achieved by having a boatyard slip the boat in a specially prepared cradle or crane it on to a hard standing. These techniques can also be useful in tidal waters, but are hardly Do-it-Yourself.

Examination by diver is probably a quick and relatively easy way to investigate a particular or suspected fault, but the execution of any work will be easier if you are standing on terra firma.

Dinghies and day boats, at least those at the smaller end of the scale, can normally be man-handled to a suitable location for examination and repair, but larger boats in tidal waters need preparation and planning. These larger boats are now considered as being of two types. The first are those with two-bilge keels, including multihulls. The second are those with one keel.

Standing on the Foreshore

Twin-bilge-keel boats and multihulls can take the bottom with no special preparation of the hull itself. What is necessary is to be sure that the bottom is good. This is best done by looking at it at the low water immediately before the high water on which you intend to take up your station.

Having carefully selected the exact part of the beach or slip on which you want your boat to settle, the next step is to ensure that you can achieve your objective. Maximum control can be exercised if you have an anchor on each quarter, each with about three boat lengths of scope, and a shore line to each bow. Unless you are particularly confident in your boat handling, it will be best to rig one of the shore lines in advance, holding the seaward end in position with a buoyed weight. When approaching the beach, drop one anchor from the stern and pick up the buoy and shore line at the bow. The second anchor and shore line can then be put in position using the dinghy. When selecting the final position, bear in mind that the sooner your boat is aground, the later she will float. This is usually the more desir-

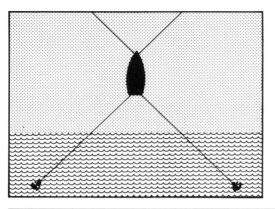

able case, but for a predictable short job (if there is such a thing), it might be more convenient to dry out later and float earlier.

When drying out any boat, do take into account the weather forecast. If there is any doubt, do not dry out. A wind-induced swell which starts while you are high and dry can become dangerous by the time the tide returns, and a bouncing boat is not a happy boat. It does not cheer the skipper either.

Improvising Legs

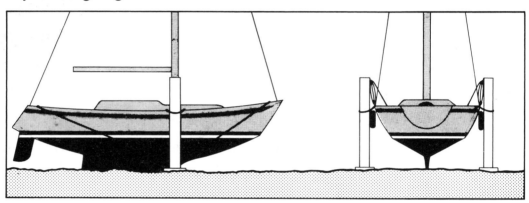

Single-keel boats with legs can be dried out in a manner similar to twin-bilge keelers. If your boat is without purpose-built legs, perhaps you can borrow a couple of decent spars for a tide or two. Decent means 4×4in (100×100mm) cross-section for a twenty-five footer, and at least 39in (1m) longer than the distance from the ground to the gunwale by the main rigging. If the bottom is soft it will be necessary to fix pads of, say, 12×12in (300×300mm) five-ply wood to the foot of each spar so that it will not sink in the sand, or whatever. Fore and aft guys should be secured near the foot of each leg and led to each end of the boat. These will be used to keep the legs vertical. Use rope strops to hold the top of each leg in position against the boat's side. These strops should be tight enough to locate the legs properly but loose enough to allow for vertical movement of the leg within it. Protect the boat's side with padding. The final move is to attach a three-

or four-part purchase between the top of each leg and a chain plate. Main sheet and kicking strap purchases often serve this purpose. As the boat settles, the purchases are used to adjust the heights of the legs so

that the boat has no list. If the keel is short and the bow tends to dip, it is advisable to put a prop under the bow, particularly if you need to walk around the deck while dried out.

Leaning on a Wall

Without legs or the availability of spars to improvise as such, the single-keel boat can be dried out by leaning it against a wall. Of course, most walls have owners, so permission should be obtained first, a formality which might also be necessary when using a beach. Incidentally, before committing yourself to drying out, it would be as well to ensure that the owner of the property, particularly if it is a boatyard, is willing for you to carry out your own work.

Of all the options, leaning on walls is the least convenient, for it means that most of one side will be inaccessible. This might lead to the only case for drying out with the bow pointing down the beach so that you can get to the other side. You will need substantial fenders – motor tyres are by far the best. With all but the smallest boats, pneumatic fenders should not be used. If, for any reason, they are used, ensure that the valves are at the bottom. If the weight of the boat forces the valves to part company with the fender you will be less likely to get a very dangerous eyeful. The boat should be given a significant, but not dramatic list of, say, 5° towards the wall. Useful ballast for this can be anchors, anchor chain and water containers (filled with water). The combination of the fendering and the list should be such that when the tyres have been squashed flat, which is almost inevitable, all the above deck fittings such as the guard-rails and stanchions and the rigging will be clear of the wall. Of course, it is possible to remove these fittings if necessary.

Greater distance from the wall or the bridging of piles can be achieved by slinging a 'leaning' spar outside of and centred on the tyres. This spar can be any substantial length of wood and is often a plank. Care should be taken to ensure that the weight of the boat is taken at strong points such as bulkheads and, if the absence of tumble home allows,

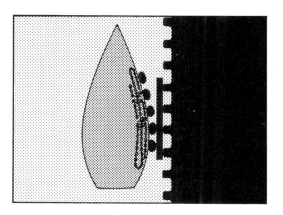

high up near the deck. All the warps, including springs and breast ropes, should be tended all the time the tide and boat are falling to avoid the tyres and leaning spar getting caught up on the wall and thus failing in their allotted tasks.

There will come a critical time when the boat is aground and leaning on the wall when the wash of a passing boat might make the water level rise sufficiently to lift the boat away from the wall or even cause it to lean the wrong way. This very real problem can be overcome by taking a mast halyard, almost certainly extended with another warp, to a strong point on the quay and using the winch or a purchase if necessary to haul the boat the right way again. This is usually surprisingly easy. If you do resort to this halyard technique, or even if you rig it

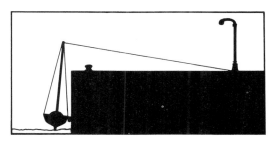

'just in case', I would strongly advise you to find a way to ensure that you remember to release it before attempting to leave the wall.

One final note, the illustration has no warps shown for reasons of clarity, but it is important to have maximum control of the boat as she is settling, and this is best achieved by use of head and stern ropes, springs and breast lines.

Cleaning the Bottom

Once the boat has settled and the ropes no longer need tending, you would be well advised to don your waders or swimsuit and set about cleaning the bottom of the hull. The growths are much more easily removed while wet. A good stiff long-handled brush, frequently dunked in the water and motivated with enthusiastic elbow-grease, will usually suffice to clear the surface fouling. If it dries before you finish, you will have to find an alternative source of water, presumably via a hose.

If you have access to a hose and do not mind the inherent risks, domestic bleach can be used to remove stubborn growth. It is best sprayed on by means of a hand-pressurised garden spray. When the growth has changed colour from green to pale yellow, it will probably fall off when hosed with fresh water. It will certainly scrub off quite easily. When using bleach, for the sake of the eyes and clothes of all concerned, including passers-by, please be careful. I must also voice an additional word of warning. It is possible that strong bleach will cause the gel coat of glass reinforced plastic to blister if it is allowed to linger. Though it is not an effect which I have observed, it is certainly worth bearing in mind.

5 Hulls

Wood

Faults

Faults in wooden hulls fall broadly into three categories: impact damage, rot and decay.

Impact Damage

The cause of this is fairly self-explanatory and the only assessment to be made of it is to determine the extent of the damage and the type of repair necessary. This can be anything from filling a shallow surface scratch to replacing several planks and frames.

Rot

This can be caused in several different ways. Electrical action, either galvanic or electrolytic, will cause not only damage to the metals directly concerned, but also, by the creation of acids and alkalis, to the adjacent wood. Fungus is also a source of rot in wood.

Galvanism When two dissimilar metals in close proximity are immersed in an electrolyte, an electric current will flow from one to the other. The lesser noble will be eaten away. An alkali will form around the nobler metal and an acid will form around the other.

An electrolyte is a liquid which will conduct electricity. Water, in its pure state, is an insulator, but the addition of impurities soon changes that. In this sense, 'fresh' water is impure and sea water even more so. Inevitably, boats spend long periods immersed in an electrolyte.

All metals have a logical place in an electro-chemical series, and it is this position which determines its 'nobility'. Part of this series follows. It illustrates the relative positions of those metals commonly used in the construction of boats. It also includes some which are not.

Platinum	Nickel
Gold	Steel
Silver	Cadmium
Monel	Iron
Bronze	Chromium
Copper	Zinc
Brass	Aluminium
Lead	Magnesium
Tin	

Those at the top of the table, such as platinum and gold, are, naturally enough, regarded as the noblest. Magnesium and aluminium are quite plebeian and thought of as least noble. If any two metals are immersed in an electrolyte, the current will flow towards the nobler, that is, the one placed higher in the table. The other will waste away. For example, if brass and steel are immersed, the current will flow from the steel towards the brass and the steel will 'corrode'. When a boat is built, efforts are usually made to use metals of similar nobility, but it is inevitable, owing to different requirements for different purposes, that the end product will contain a mixture. Once such a mixture is immersed in water, galvanic action will start.

Stop it we cannot, control it we can. By introducing a metal of lesser nobility than any used in the construction, we ensure that all the corrosion is confined to this new metal. When a current flows between two metals in an electrolyte, it is said to flow from an anode to a cathode. Zinc or one of its derivatives is often the relatively ignoble metal introduced to act as the anode and consequently to waste away before any of the structural metals. It is a 'sacrificial' anode. Such anodes are available in a multitude of shapes and sizes to satisfy many requirements. They can be of a simple rectangular shape to be attached to the hull, or of another type intended to be secured around a propeller shaft, for instance.

Electrolysis When a 'stray' electric current flows through the fittings of a boat to 'earth', in this case the water, the metal fittings through which the current passes will act as an anode and waste away in a manner similar to that caused by galvanic action. However, the source of the electric current is quite different and sacrificial anodes will have no effect with this sort of action unless they are connected electrically with all the skin fittings.

Leakage of electricity in this form is a fault condition, often due to poor wiring or damp or wet battery terminals. If electrolytic action is suspected, the whole electrical system should be checked thoroughly, suspect terminals remade, suspect wire renewed and the battery cleaned, particularly its terminals. Electrical systems on boats should always be of the two-wire type, never the earth-return system used in cars.

It is important to appreciate the difference between galvanism and electrolysis in order that a particular problem can be either controlled or corrected. However, once either of these faults has occurred the problems are very similar. In both cases, the metal from which the current flows will be wasted away and the wood surrounding it will have been attacked by the acid produced. In the case of galvanic action there will also be a metal which has been 'receiving' the current. This second metal will be surrounded by an alkali which will also have attacked the wood.

If any metal has been corroded significantly, whether it is a skin fitting or a fastening, it will have to be replaced.

Wood which has been attacked by acid or alkali will be dark and crumbly, to the point where it is useless. The only cure is to remove the affected wood completely and replace it with new, along with new fastenings, where appropriate. Whether the hole remaining after removal of the decayed wood can be plugged or whether a whole plank or more will need replacing can only be determined by the extent of the rot.

Nail sickness is the name given to the above problem when it is the plank-to-frame fastening wasting away, perhaps to the point where the planks are hardly attached to the frames. The extent of this problem can only be assessed by withdrawing sample fastenings. The first clue to the presence of nail sickness will probably be a rust-coloured stain showing through the paint. Owing to a variable moisture content of the wood, it might be found to exist over a limited area. When the exact extent of the problem has been established and all the rot removed, the alternatives will be either to plug the holes and refasten into the frames adjacent to the original fastenings or renew whole or parts of planks. It is possible that as your investigation proceeds you will find rot in the frames themselves. Should this be the case, once more the rot must be removed completely. If up to about one-sixth of the width of the frame has to be removed, it will be sufficient to set alongside a fillet of dimensions equal to those of the original frame. If possible, the new planking should be fastened to both old and new frames. If significantly more than about one-sixth of the width of the frame has to be removed it will be necessary to remove the affected part completely, scarf in a new section and set in fillets alongside the joints.

Nail sickness is more likely to be encountered in older boats with galvanised iron fastenings. It is possible to find it with brass and mild steel fastenings, but most unlikely with those of bronze or monel. Most woods have a metal content which aggravates the galvanic action problem, so attempts should have been made during construction to match the fastening material to the timber.

Wet Rot A high moisture content in timber can lead to microscopic fungoid attack. The rotten wood becomes dark or even black. When still wet, it is of a sponge-like texture and easily compressed. If it has dried it is easily crumbled. Once again, complete removal and replacement of the affected wood is the only cure. Likely areas where wet rot is found are where fresh water has been allowed to stand on unpainted wood. It could be rain water behind or under fittings such as chain plates or on the lands of clinker planks. It could be condensation in lockers or rain water in the bilge. By virtue of its cause, wet rot is more likely to be found on the inside of a hull than outside.

This problem could be eliminated completely by covering all the wood in the boat with an unbroken surface of paint. Of course, this is a practical impossibility, so the best compromise is to paint where at all possible and ensure adequate and frequent ventilation elsewhere. If the air is not allowed to stagnate, thus avoiding condensation, the problem will probably be avoided. Regular scrubbing of the decks with sea water will avoid the problem there and, if it does not happen of its own accord, keeping a small amount of sea water in the bilge should look after that area.

Decay

Being eaten by parasites is the most common cause of wood decay. There are two worms of major interest to wooden-boat owners: gribble and teredo.

Gribble This small worm, usually about ⅛ in (3mm) long, lives in salt water. Given the opportunity, it will eat its way through the surface of the wood for a short distance and then return to the surface, only to repeat the journey a short distance into the wood before returning to the surface once again.

Left to its own devices, it will carry on in this way, aided by its colleagues, until the area near the surface is so crumbly that it is washed away by the movement of the water. This exposes a fresh surface which will then satisfy the immediate hunger requirements of the worms. Unchecked, the gribble will, in time, eat all the wood available. The only cure is to remove completely the affected part, gribble and all, and renew the wood. The problem can be prevented by maintaining a sound coat of paint. Though it will never eat its way through paint, the gribble is not averse to shouldering its way through the smallest of cracks in its search for food.

Teredo This second worm can be anything from ¾ in (20mm) to 6½ ft (2m) long, the length appearing to be related to the temperature of the water. The teredo usually, but by no means exclusively, eats into the wood by way of the end grain. Once in the wood, unlike the gribble, it shows no inclination to eat through the surface, but is content to work its way up and down the inside of the planks. If the problem passes unnoticed for long enough, this can lead to the plank collapsing. Once again, it is a sound coating of paint which will keep the teredo at bay. Common places where the worm gets in are the end grain of the planks near the deadwood, rudder trunks or other associated places which are often difficult to antifoul and the centre-board casing of dinghies. One other possible point of entry is in or near plank seams where working of the caulking has lifted and cracked the antifoul paint. The sign of entry is just a group of holes, the diameter of which is related to the size of the worm, of course. In northern European waters this is often only about ¹⁄₁₆ in (1mm). The cure is to remove all the affected wood.

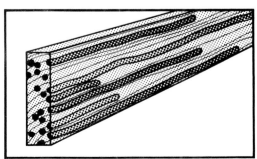

Because the worms live in salt water, a boat infested with them can be relieved of the long-term problem by either taking the boat to a fresh-water environment or removing it from the water completely, in either case for a period of two weeks or so. This action, though it will kill off the worms already in the wood, does nothing to rectify the damage they have already caused.

Delamination

Plywood When used in boat construction, plywood is frequently bent to take up a desired shape. The bending inevitably creates a tension in the outer skin which can result in cracking which, in turn, will crack

the paint and allow water to come in contact with the wood. A similar problem can occur with the inner skin, the only difference being one of principle in that this will have been caused by compression. Ingress of water by these or any other means can lead to a weakening of the laminate glue causing the laminates to part company. The cure for delamination of plywood is to replace the affected sheet with another, preferably of marine ply marked BS 1088 WBP, indicating that it is both water- and boil-proof. Maintaining a sound coat of paint will minimise the problem.

Cold Moulding Delamination of the plies of a cold-moulded hull can occur if the glue is not protected from the water by a sound coat of paint, or perhaps from impact damage. However it is caused, the affected areas of the veneers will have to be removed and renewed.

Repairs

Repairs to the hulls of wooden boats, unless of a very minor nature, involve the removal of fastenings to enable wood to be removed. Hull planks have fastenings through themselves into or through frames. In clinker construction there are additional fastenings through the overlaps of the planks.

Fastenings

The easiest way to remove fastenings is to

have an appreciation of how they were inserted initially.

Screws The most common screw used for the fastening of wood is that with a countersunk slotted head. Wood screws have a pointed end and are threaded for about 60 per cent of the length. The size of a screw is specified by gauge and length. The gauge of a countersunk screw can be ascertained by measuring the diameter of the head in sixteenths of an inch, subtracting one from that number of sixteenths and doubling the answer. For example, if the diameter of the head is measured as ⅜ in, that is taken to be ⁶⁄₁₆ in. Subtract 1 from the 6 leaving 5; 5 multiplied by 2 equals 10. It is a 10 gauge screw. The length of a screw is measured from its tip to the surface of the wood into which it is screwed. In the case of a countersunk screw this will be its overall length.

Common fastenings

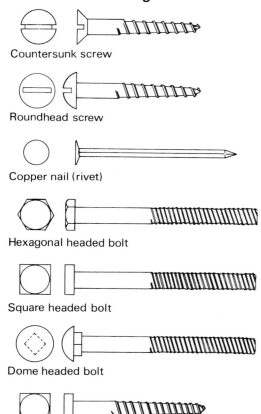

Countersunk screw

Roundhead screw

Copper nail (rivet)

Hexagonal headed bolt

Square headed bolt

Dome headed bolt

Coach screw

The wood into which the screw is fastened should be drilled with a pilot hole a little shorter than the length of the threaded part of the screw. The wood through which the screw passes and is to be the 'attached' wood should have a clearance hole of a diameter a little greater than that of the unthreaded shank of the screw. For a countersunk screw it is also necessary to drill out the top of the

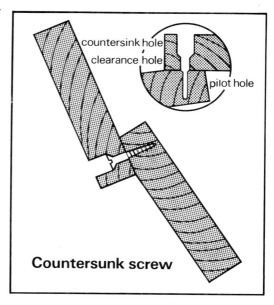

Countersunk screw

clearance hole with a countersunk bit. In order that all the threaded part of the screw is in the supporting wood, it might be necessary to countersink deeper than just the amount to take the head. The head of the screw is often concealed by covering it with a stopper or a plug of wood. Wooden plugs are usually drilled out of similar wood to that through which the screw passes and, if a very good fit, are ideally suited to surfaces which will be varnished. Yellow metal screws should be greased before driving them home and it might be advantageous, if the wood is particularly hard, to run a steel screw in first.

If a screw proves difficult to extract, try one or more of the following: (a) Tighten the screw just enough to 'start' it. This reduces the chances of burring the undoing side of the screwdriver slot. (b) With a screwdriver well seated in the slot, hit the end with a hammer or mallet, as appropriate. (c) Apply heat to the head. If it is important to avoid damaging the wood surrounding the screw this can be done with a soldering iron.

Nails When used in boat building, nails are usually clenched. The nails, almost exclusively of copper, are chosen or cut off to be of such a length that an appropriate length protrudes through the wood. A short length of the point is bent through 90° and then the rest of the protruding part hammered into the wood across the grain. The end result is something like a staple. To remove a clenched nail the staple part has to be removed. This can be done either by straightforward drilling or by using a pointed carborundum stone in a power drill. In either case, a lot of care is necessary to avoid damage to the surrounding wood. If the end is levered up, it will probably break off. If not, nip it off flush with the wood. Use a punch of a slightly smaller size than the nail to drive it out just far enough to get a purchase on the head. Use a claw hammer or something similar to remove the nail, and use a scrap of wood under the fulcrum to prevent damage to the wood.

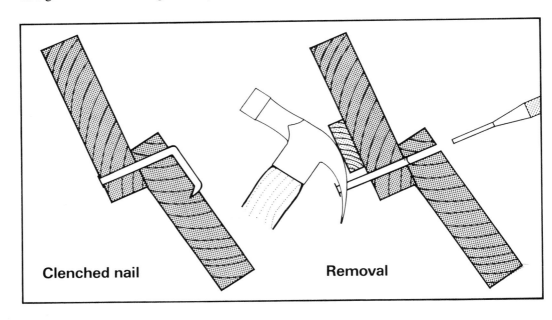

Clenched nail   **Removal**

Riveting is another way of securing nails and is a two-man job. Nails are of square cross-section and the first step is to drill a hole right through both planks or the plank and frame, whichever is appropriate. The hole should be slightly smaller than 'across the flats' of the rivet. When fastening carvel planks, it is normal to countersink the head of the rivet about ¼ in (6mm). The man outside the hull drives the rivet fully home, using a punch if necessary, and then holds a dolly against the head. If the majority of the rivets bend, try a slightly larger hole. If none bend, it is probable that the hole is too big. It is a futile pastime trying to use straightened rivets. If they have been bent once they should be scrapped. The man on the inside slips a roove over the rivet, concave side towards the wood, nips off the surplus to within about ¹⁄₁₆in (1mm) of the roove and then flattens the end over the roove, using a ball hammer. The roove should not be flattened – it needs to act as a spring.

To remove a rivet, the head over the roove should be filed off and then the rivet driven out with a punch in a manner similar to that employed with nails. The temptation to drive out the rivet completely with the punch should be resisted. The chances of the wood splitting are very high. A cutting disc fitted to an electric drill can be used to remove the heads of the rivets, but a lot of care is required if the wood is not to be damaged.

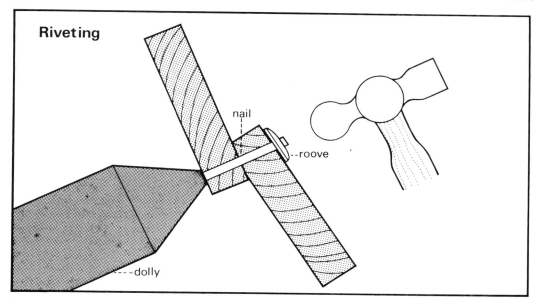

Riveting

Bolts These are often used for large jobs such as fastening fillets to frames or when doubling up frames. Those with hexagonal or square heads and similar nuts are usually relatively easy to remove once a spanner can be applied to each end. Those with a domed head which rely on a squared section of the shank below the head to dig into the wood and supply enough friction usually do so when the bolt is tightened, but, just as often, particularly if the wood has become wet and soft, fail to supply the friction when it is time to remove the bolt. The head will turn in the wood. Three possible ways of removing the nut are: (1) Hold the head with a wrench, though this often necessitates damaging the wood around the head. (2) Apply heat to the nut and remove it while hot. If the wood is not to be damaged it is probably better to use a large soldering iron than a blow torch. (3) Cut a 'screwdriver' slot across the head.

Coach Screws Once again, these are usually used for fairly heavy work. Coach screws consist of a pointed tip, from which they are threaded for about three-quarters of the length to a square head. It is necessary to drill a clearance hole the length of the unthreaded shank and a pilot hole the diameter of threaded shank. Coach screws are turned into the wood with a spanner and are not usually difficult to remove.

Fastening Material To make an assessment of the correct material to choose for a particular fastening, it might be advisable to refer to the electro-chemical series described earlier, but in the absence of any information to the contrary, you would be well advised to use a similar material to that used by the manufacturer.

Adhesives Though available in a bewildering number of types with an equal number of names, it is probably true to say that, from among modern products, there are only two types which need concern the boat repairer: (a) those based on urea-formaldehyde resins; (b) those based on resorcinol-phenol-form-aldehyde resin.

(a) These synthetic resin glues produce a gap-filling, water-resistant glue with a high resistance to moisture and fungi. Available in two forms, the first, such as Cascamite Powdered Resin Glue, is available in powder form to which the hardener has already been added. It is simply mixed with cold water and is then ready for use, with a life of about three hours. The second form, such as Aerolite 306, though in powder form, is supplied with a separate hardener. The powder is mixed with cold water and then added to one of the surfaces to be joined. The hardener is added to the other surface. The chemical action leading to the setting of the glue starts as soon as the two surfaces are brought into contact, and the surfaces should not be moved more than twenty minutes or so after that action has started.

One advantage of this second form is that the liquid glue will remain serviceable for about three months. In the powder form, the shelf life is about two years, and that of the hardener is three years.

(b) These resin glues, such as Aerodux 500, are available with three grades of resin which, when mixed with the hardener, will give a choice of pot life of anything from one to four hours at normal temperatures. Aerodux adhesives are particularly useful when working with materials of high moisture content and 'difficult' timbers such as teak. However, they are also relatively expensive and are not available in small quantities, so most readers will probably find that one of the urea-formaldehyde resin glues will serve.

Having determined the extent of the damage to the hull by cutting out all the rotten wood and removing planks where necessary, it will be seen that the repair might be anything from filling a surface scratch to renewing several planks and frames. These possibilities are now considered in ascending order of magnitude. In reality, any one repair is likely to need a combination of two or more of the following techniques.

Surface Irregularities

Having been cleared of all loose flakes of wood and paint, the area should be painted with a metallic primer and when that is dry, it should be filled with a dressing cement or trowel cement. The filler should be rubbed smooth with a block and 230 grade wet and dry paper used dry.

Fastening Holes

If at any time when fastenings are being removed they break off flush with the wood, just leave them, but ensure that new fastenings are not offered up in the same place. Having removed a few fastenings and discovered minimal damage, it might be necessary simply to fill a few holes vacated by the fastenings. Before filling, all rotten wood must be removed, perhaps using a tool like a bradawl, until the hole is surrounded by clean wood, and then all the bare wood must be primed.

When the priming paint is dry, the hole can be filled with a glass-fibre paste; or if a fastening is to go through the same hole, use a polyester resin such as Plastic Padding, through which a new fastening could be driven, before finally filling with more resin.

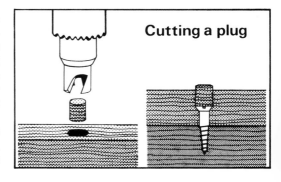

Cutting a plug

When the resin is hard, it should be rubbed smooth.

If the surface is to be varnished, the colour of the resin will probably be unacceptable unless a good match can be achieved by mixing an appropriate sawdust with it. If that will not work, the only alternative is to set in wooden plugs of the same timber as the surface. Ensure that the plugs are cut across the grain, then drill out the countersunk holes to the same diameter. The overlength plugs should be glued with a synthetic resin and then tapped firmly home. When the glue has hardened, plane off the surplus plug.

Various techniques to suit various circumstances can be used for the measuring, shaping and joining of wood. For example, frames can be shaped in three ways: sawing, steam bending and laminating. The joining of two pieces of wood can be effected using butt or scarf joints. It will be as well to consider the individual techniques before embarking on the specific repairs.

Measuring and Marking

Boats are made up entirely of irregularly shaped pieces, or so it seems. When renewing one of the pieces, the measuring of the shape is the first problem to be encountered. When it is not practicable to offer up the new wood for marking, one of three variations on the theme of spiling should overcome the problem.

Making a Template for a Frame On a piece of stiff board or plywood, from which the template will be cut, draw a series of parallel lines at 3in (75mm) intervals. Tack this board in a position adjacent to the frame to be measured, perhaps on a deck beam. From scrap wood cut a 'spiling' stick, long enough to reach from both sides of the frame to the board. Make one end of this stick a right angle and the other a point. Offer up the spiling stick so that the upper edge is along one of the parallel lines and the point is against the inside edge of the frame. On the board, mark the position of the upper corner of the spiling stick on the line. Repeat for each line, then repeat the whole process for

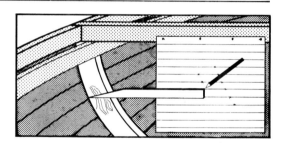

the other edge of the frame, this time offering up the point of the spiling stick to the planks. Take down the board, draw a smooth curve through the marked points, using a batten perhaps, and cut out the template.

Marking a Large Area An alternative which lends itself better to the marking of large areas such as a dinghy foredeck is as follows.

A similar spiling stick is used, but this time it will be an advantage if it is quite wide, say, 2-3in (50-75mm). A spiling board is fixed inside the area to be measured. Lay the spiling stick on the board and offer up the point to the edge where the deck will go. Mark around one corner of the spiling stick. Repeat the offering up and marking at

frequent intervals. Always mark the same corner and do not worry about the apparently random pattern of the marks, just make a lot of them. Transfer the spiling board to the new plywood. Lay the spiling stick on the spiling board so that the corner lines up with one of the marks. On the new plywood mark the position of the point. Repeat with all the other marks. Draw a fair curve through all the marks on the new plywood, again using a batten, and cut out your foredeck.

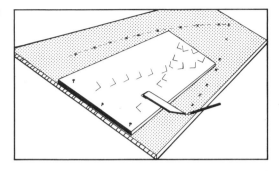

Making a Frame If the old frame is still sufficiently well formed it can be used as a template for the new, otherwise a board template will have to be made. It should fit the hull exactly, but be generous with all lengths. Trimming to size is always quicker and easier than starting again.

Sawn Frame

For DIY purposes, the sawing of frames is only practicable for short lengths. The template is used to mark directly on to the new wood. Make sure the grain of the wood follows the curve of the frame; a grain which 'runs out' of the curve will be too weak to be useful.

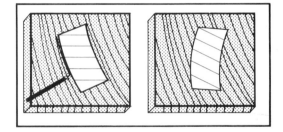

Steam Bending

The only safe way to bend timber without it breaking is to first immerse it in steam until it becomes soft and pliable. The box to contain the steam can be made of wood or from a length of pipe. It should have bridge supports for the timber so that it can be completely enveloped by the steam. The source of steam needs to be of a size compatible to that of the box, and could be anything from a kettle to an electric clothes-boiler. In use, the box should have a slight inclination and the lower end through which the steam is fed should also have a drain hole. It is unlikely that it would be so, but it is worth stressing that the system should not be so steam-tight that high pressures are achieved. How long the steaming will take is dependent on the type and size of the wood, but it will probably be longer than you think. For the smallest length it will probably take an hour or more, certainly long enough to have a cup of tea and get on with the next step.

Transfer the curve from the template to a proportionately substantial board, perhaps

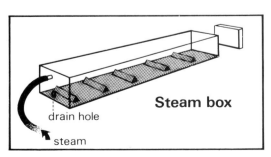

Steam box

drain hole

steam

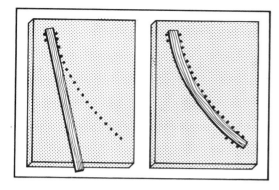

even the floor of a shed if the size of frame warrants it. Drive a fence of heavy nails vertically into the inner curve. When the timber is sufficiently steamed, that is, when it can be manipulated without fighting, one end is located at one end of the fence with a couple of nails and then it is bent around the curve and the other end located. When the timber has dried it will usually straighten a little, so it is quite in order to set the curve of the former slightly tighter than that of the template. Small pieces or timber can sometimes be bent after immersing in boiling water and in some cases even cold water.

Laminating a Frame

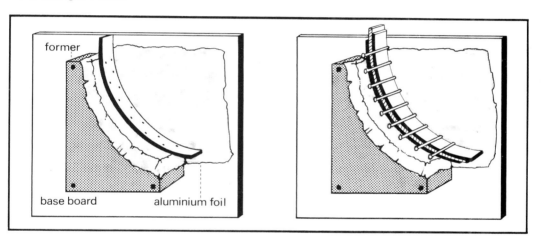

This is probably the best, easiest and strongest way of making a frame. The template is used to make a former which is thicker than the finished frame will be. This former is secured to a suitable base board. The laminates should be generously long and about 1/8–3/16 in (2–3mm) thick. To prevent the laminations being glued to either the former or the base board, this area is covered with aluminium foil. The first laminate is tacked to the former using brass brads. A synthetic resin glue should be used to fix the next lamination which will be held firmly in place by nails driven vertically into the base board. Subsequent laminations are glued and added, moving the retaining nails one at a time to keep all the laminations closed up hard. When the right thickness has been achieved, the frame should be left undisturbed for as long as possible. Though careful handling is probably possible after about six hours, remember that it might be several days before maximum strength has been achieved. When all the laminations have been added, if there is any sign that the nails are not holding them all in position properly, you can always apply more clamps. When the frame is removed from the former, the original brass brads should be trimmed neatly.

Marking a Plank

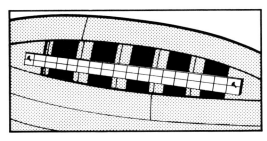

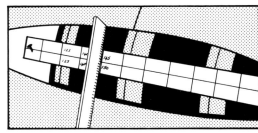

1 Cut a batten thinner and longer than the required plank. Draw along it the long centre line and at right angles to that draw more lines at intervals of about 3in (75mm). Tack this batten over the hole such that it is about in the middle and overlapping both ends.

2 Measure the two distances along a cross line, from the centre line to the edges of the planks immediately above and below the hole. Note these two dimensions on the batten adjacent to the appropriate cross line. Repeat for each cross line.

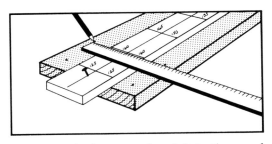

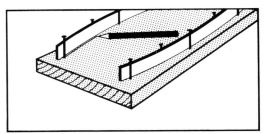

3 Remove the batten and tack it to the wood which is to become the new plank. Mark off the dimensions from the centre line, along the cross lines on to the new plank.

4 Erect a fence of nails to follow the line of the curve of the marks, bend and secure a flexible batten around it. Draw a line around the batten. Repeat for the other side. Cut out the plank.

Butt Joints

Scarf Joints

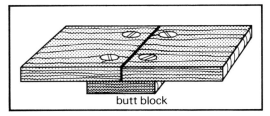

butt block

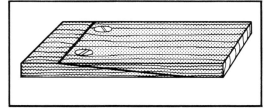

For these, the simplest of joints, the ends of, say, the planks to be joined should be squared off as near perfectly as possible. The joint should be backed up with a square block the same width and thickness as the planks, bedded in mastic and then screwed to the planks.

The advantage of a scarf joint is that the much larger surface-to-surface contact area allows for a much stronger glued joint than the simple butt. The angle you can cut for the scarf will usually be limited by circumstances, but if it is possible, a slope of about 1 in 10 is worth aiming for. It might be necessary to hold down the ends of the scarfs with screws, at least until the glue has set.

Caulking

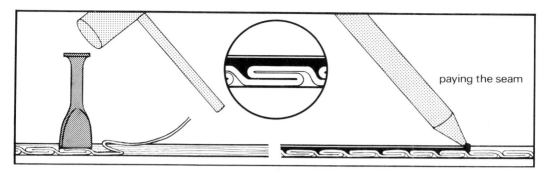

paying the seam

If the caulking is to be renewed, the old should be raked out thoroughly with the aid of a hook – perhaps the bent and sharpened handle of an old file – until new clean wood is seen. The seam should then be painted with a priming paint.

Caulking cotton is usually supplied in balls of loosely laid-up strands. You will need to add or subtract strands to suit the size of your seams. How much to add or subtract will, initially at least, be discovered by trial and error, so be prepared to remove occasional lengths in order to change the number of strands so the 'packing' is just right. If you have to add strands, aim to lay it up to about the same tension as the original. Roll it in the palms of the hands or, if the length justifies it, secure the distant end and lock yours in the chuck of a twist drill and 'wind' it up.

A caulking iron, similar to a builder's bolster and a mallet, is used to force the cotton into the seams. The first couple of inches are tapped in, then a loop is laid back over that length and tapped in on top of it, making three layers in all. It would be normal for a shipwright to loosely fill the full length in this manner and then go back to the beginning and 'harden' the whole seam. The newcomer would be advised to harden more frequently to ensure that the correct amount of cotton is being forced in. As the cotton is driven down hard into the V between the planks, they will open slightly and then close again, gripping the cotton firmly. When the cotton is hard, it should be within about $\frac{3}{16}$in (3mm) of the surface. If there is too much, pull out the offending length, remove a strand or more and carry on. If there is too little, pull out the required length, roll in another strand or more, and then continue. If you try laying separate strands on top of the others, you will find that they will not be gripped by the planks.

If only a section needs to be caulked, pull out the good caulking for about 39in (1m), separate the strands and cut them to different lengths, do the same with the new cotton and marry them together. A similar technique should be used at the end. The gap between the cotton and the surface is 'payed' with a synthetic rubber compound, normally sold in tubes with a nozzle which, when cut to a size appropriate to your seams, makes for a relatively easy job. Once the paying has set, the surplus should be removed as recommended by the manufacturers.

Clinker Planks

When all the rotten or damaged wood has been removed, the extent of the repair required will be seen. If a number of planks is to be replaced in the same area, all the joins should be staggered as much as possible. The ends of any one section to be replaced will coincide with frames and these ends should be tapered as accurately as possible as the first step towards scarf joints which will be centred on the frames. The taper should be such that the longest measurement for the replacement plank is on

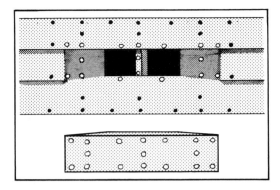

the outside of the hull. With clinker planks, these tapers can only be cut properly with a lot of patience and perhaps a block plane, spokeshave or chisel. If there is much of a curve in the plank it might need to be steam bent before any other shaping is attempted. If there is a curve in the second plane, this will then have to be shaped with a plane or by sanding. The upper outer edge of the plank, that is, the 'corner' which meets the plank above it, is often chamfered to allow the planks to follow the curve of the hull. Examine the old plank for details of this and then chamfer the new.

When the new plank is as near to the right

shape as you can get it, the taper should be put on one end. When that appears to be a good fit – and remember that you probably will not be able to offer it up completely – taper the other end. You should now be able to offer it up and if liberal quantities of blue chalk are applied to all the mating surfaces, you should find all the high spots. Whatever you do, do not be over-enthusiastic when removing the high spots, for it is but a short step back to the page about measuring.

When the fit is as good as you can get it – and remember that it is all a waste of time if, at the end of the day, the boat leaks – the final preparation can be made before fastening. All the parts which will be hidden once the plank is fitted should be painted with a priming paint. Varnish thinned with white spirit can be used if the hull is to be varnished. When the priming is dry, the new section should be drilled and countersunk with all the holes which will be needed to fasten it to or through the frames at its ends, any other frames it will cross and to the edges of the planks above and below. The ends of the scarfs might need holding down with small screws which, if countersunk, can be hidden with stopper. Finally, glue the scarfs before fastening.

Carvel Planks

Though carvel planks would be better replaced with scarf joints, it is usually the case that butts are used. This is probably because not only is the joint itself easier, but it is usually easy to apply blocks and battens to all the seams and joins inside the hull to improve the strength and water-keeping qualities.

The new plank can be measured and shaped in the manner already described. When it is finally cut to length, the ends should be square. A major difference in the method of construction is the way in which carvel planks are made watertight. The seams between the planks are 'caulked', usually with cotton, but large vessels use oakum. To make room for this caulking, the outer half of the edges of the planks are chamfered so that when the planks are in position there is a V-shaped gap for half the

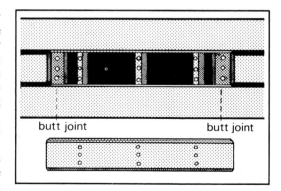

butt joint   butt joint

thickness of the planks, open to the outside. For details of the chamfer, the adjacent good planks can be examined.

It is as well, particularly if there is any significant curve in the plank, to make the length of the replacement section at least as long as the spacing between three of the frames. Because the butt joint will rely on a block behind it on the inside of the hull to make it watertight, the joints must come between the frames.

If a short section of plank with a curve is to be replaced, it might be easier to fashion it out of a thicker piece of wood than it would be to bend the short piece. When the plank is ready to be fastened, its edges and ends should be painted with primer paint and the relevant holes drilled to enable it to be fastened to each frame over which it passes and also to fasten to it the butt blocks at each end. These butt blocks should be the same width and thickness as the planks and approximately square. If they will be seen

when the repair is finished, it will be as well to chamfer the edges of the blocks before fitting them. The blocks should be bedded in mastic and it is better to attach them to the existing planks before attempting to fasten the new section.

When the fastening has been completed the seams are caulked. If there is any chance of the new, probably unseasoned wood shrinking, it would be a wise precaution to fix battens over the inside seams between the old and new wood, these also being bedded in mastic. If this battening has been anticipated sufficiently far in advance, the butt blocks will have been recessed to take the battens.

Tingles

A simple way to repair a small hole or fracture of a plank is to fix a patch of wood over it. This 'tingle' should be bedded in mastic. The appearance of this basically unattractive repair can be marginally improved by making the tingle larger than is structurally necessary and then give it long chamfers to fair it in.

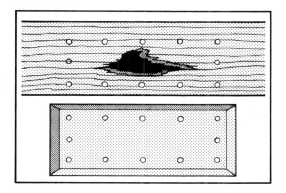

Plywood

The best way to repair plywood is to remove the damaged panel completely and, using the old one as a template, cut out a completely new one. Before fastening, thoroughly seal the edges with paint or varnish, preferably with several coats, for it is water getting in between the laminations which is one of the biggest problems with boats built of plywood. Fasten the new section to the frames in the same manner as the old section was.

A smaller hole can be repaired as follows. Cut out all the damage until the remaining wood is sound. Make the hole a regular shape, preferably with right-angled corners, using a pad saw or an electric jigsaw. The regular shape and corners are only to make the cutting of the replacement piece easier. Chamfer the edges so that the hole is larger on the outside of the hull than it is inside.

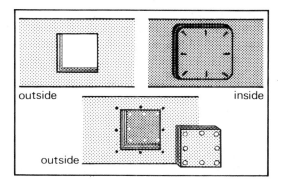

This can be done when enlarging the hole or it can now be achieved with a file. Inside the hull, glue and fix with clenched nails a pad about 1½in (40mm) larger all round than the hole. Cut and chamfer the patch to the correct size and then seal the edges as before.

Hulls

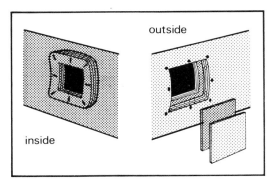

The patch is then glued, nailed and clenched to the pad.

If the damage is on a curved section, a hole of adequate size in the centre of the pad to be fixed inside of the hull will allow it to bend to take up the shape of the hull as it is nailed and clenched. The patch must now be built up with successive layers of glued veneers, the final one being nailed and clenched through the pad.

Cold Moulding

For this method of construction, a mould is set up and over it is laid diagonally a wide strip of veneer. A second veneer is glued to the first, laying it on the other diagonal. Third and subsequent layers are added, changing the diagonal each time, until the design thickness has been reached.

Damage not completely penetrating the hull can be repaired as follows. Mark a regular shape around the damaged area. Use a steel rule and a sharp knife to cut through the first veneer. A chisel, bevel side down and used gently, will enable the damaged skin to be prised off. If the damage extends into the next layer, mark another smaller regular shape, then cut and remove that one as you did the first. Carry on removing veneers until you come to a good one, making each successive portion removed a little smaller than its predecessor. Next, cut the requisite number of veneers, each to its own size, ensuring that the grain runs at right angles to that of the veneer to which it will be attached. Glue them in position in sequence. The final veneer can be held in position with weights or, if that is not practicable, with staples fired across the edges with a staple gun. When the glue has set, the staples can be removed and an application of hot water will close the holes.

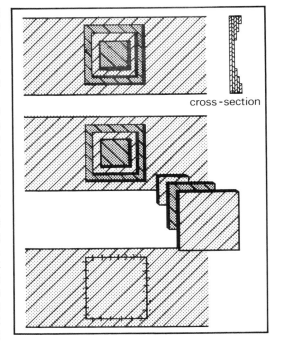

cross-section

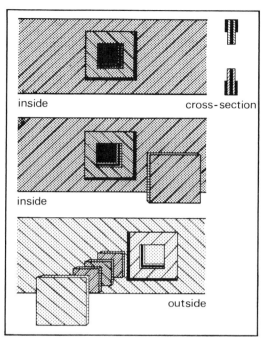

inside

cross-section

inside

outside

If the hull has been holed completely, it can be repaired as follows. First, cut out all the damaged section and then enlarge it to a regular shape. Then cut from each of the veneers on the inside and outside of the hull similar but larger shapes. Matching the grains, cut two portions for the inside and outside veneers, and cut enough, all the same size as the smaller hole, to fill it. Using weights or staples to hold it in place, glue the outer veneer in place. When the glue has set, built up the middle section with veneers and glue. When the middle section has set, the inner veneer can be glued and stapled if necessary. All gaps should be filled with glue.

It might be found easier, if a 'bulge' on the inside of the hull is acceptable, to repair a hole using GRP techniques, mat and resin.

Sprung Planks

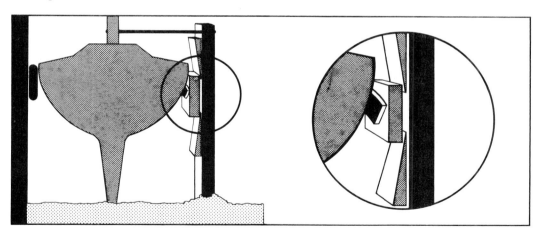

When removing fastenings for examination, there is a chance that the plank will 'spring'. When renewing a plank, in spite of steam bending, it is often necessary to force the plank in. In all these cases, there are various ways in which the problem can be overcome.

If the wood is substantial enough, screw an eye into the inside of the plank and attach a Spanish windlass purchase to a suitable point on the other side of the hull. The suitable point might well be another screw eye. If that method is not suitable, an alternative can be tried from outside the hull.

Assuming the boat to be on hard standing, a substantial timber should be stood in a firm base vertically below the offending end of the plank, but a little away from the boat. A firm base could be established by digging into the ground or surrounding the bottom of the timber with sand, rocks, etc. The upper end of the timber should be secured to the deck with appropriate padding and lash-ings. If the timber is now fairly rigid and in line with the end of the plank, pads and wedges can be used to force the plank home.

Frames

As already stated when discussing the ways of shaping wood, and frames in particular, there are basically three standards of frame repair: (1) setting in a fillet; (2) scarfing in a replacement length and reinforcing the joints with fillets; (3) doubling or replacing the whole frame.

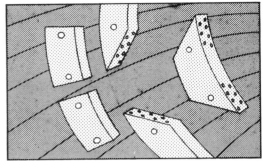

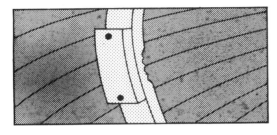

(1) If the weakened frame has not had removed from it more than about one-sixth of its cross-sectional area, all that is required is to reinforce that area with a fillet, the dimensions of which are the same as the original frame. The fillet should be through fastened to the original frame and the planks should be fastened to both old and new frames.

(2) To scarf in a new section, it is first necessary to remove all the damaged wood and then cut neat scarfs at the ends of the original frames. The new section which, it is hoped, is of generous length, can then be offered up alongside one of the gaps and the angle of one of the scarfs marked. When this scarf has been cut, the section can be offered up again and the second scarf marked and cut. But be generous. With luck, the section will need trimming rather than remaking. When the fit is really snug, the new section can be drilled to take appropriate screws and the original can be drilled with pilot holes. The glue is then applied and the section screwed home. Fillets should then be set alongside both scarf joints and through bolted to the original frames on both sides of each joint.

(3) Assuming that there is a substantial amount of the original frame left when all the damage has been removed, it is probably easier to double the whole frame than it is to remove the original. Once again, it will be necessary to through fasten the old to the new and add plank fastenings to the new.

Glass Reinforced Plastic (GRP)

Construction

The plastic is a rigid, but quite brittle, poly-ester resin. The reinforcing glass, in the form of very fine fibres, has high tensile strength but is very floppy. The combination of brittle resin and floppy glass-fibres produces a material which is both strong and rigid.

When newly manufactured, the resin is liquid, of about the same viscosity as a thick paint. Left to its own devices for some years it will cure and become solid, a process which is irreversible. By the addition of a suitable catalyst or hardener, this curing period can be reduced to about thirty minutes at normal temperatures. The basic resin is translucent, but when used as the outer skin of the hull of a boat it is normally coloured by the addition of pigments. This coloured resin is the gel coat.

The glass-fibres, the diameter of each of which is much less than that of a human hair, are used in three different forms: (1) Numerous fibres are laid up parallel to each other in strands or rovings which are then woven together. By varying the number of fibres in the rovings and the density of the weave, various types can be made to suit various purposes. The type most commonly used for repairs is of a fairly open weave and is known simply as a 'woven roving'. (2) Rovings with significantly less fibres in them are 'chopped off' at intervals of about 2in (50mm) and allowed to fall in a random manner on to a moving surface. In so doing, a 'mat' is formed. This 'chopped strand mat' is held together with a binding agent which will eventually be dissolved by the resin. (3) Long individual fibres are 'flaked' into a very fine layer, a number of which are laid up together to make a tissue. This fine, soft tissue is a 'surfacing tissue'.

Hulls may be constructed with GRP by either of two methods: (1) by laying up layers of glass and resin on a mound; (2) by laying up layers of glass and resin on either side of a foam to make a 'sandwich'. The first of these techniques is better suited to mass production, whereas the second is

quicker and easier if only one hull is required.

Moulded

The first step towards moulding a hull is to make a 'plug', exactly the same shape and size of the intended hull. This plug is usually made of wood and finished with many layers of paint and filler. The object is to make the surface as near to perfect as possible, for any defects in the plug will find their way through to the finished hull. The second step is to produce the 'mould'. This is an 'inside-out' boat, made by laying up layers of resin-impregnated glass mat around the plug. In order to be able to release the mould from the plug a release agent is added. This can be a wax polish or PVA (polyvinyl alcohol). The first layer of resin is brushed or perhaps sprayed on to the plug, to be followed by as many layers of mat and resin as are necessary to make a rigid mould. Reinforcing struts may be added in order that the mould will be absolutely inflexible when it is eventually turned on to its bottom. When the mould has hardened it is removed from the plug and any further defects made good. Finally, it is given a mirror-like finish by polishing. The mould is then ready to be used to produce any number of hulls.

To produce a hull, the mould is first treated with a release agent, probably a wax polish, to which the gel coat will not adhere. The gel coat is brushed or sprayed on to form the outer skin of the finished hull. This gel coat is quite brittle, as are all resin coats. Because the hull needs to have an amount of flexibility, this gel coat is limited to a thickness of 350–500 microns, so reducing the chances of it cracking as a result of small movements.

Before the gel coat has hardened completely, a layer of surfacing tissue is applied and then thoroughly impregnated with resin. Subsequent layers of mat and resin are added until the designed thickness of hull has been achieved.

Faults

Impact damage

This form of damage can vary from simple dirt stains to holes penetrating right through the hull. All damaged gel coat, crumbling or flaking resin and glass must be removed before a full assessment of the damage can be made. When this has been done, it will be seen that the damage falls into one of four categories: a surface abrasion; a crack; a mat fracture; a hull puncture.

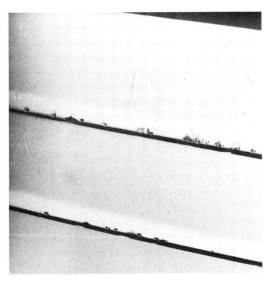

Air Bubbles

During manufacture, a gel coat is applied to the mould first, and then layers of mat and resin are added. Each layer of mat should be thoroughly impregnated with resin and all air bubbles removed. If this 'laying up' has not been performed correctly, or if an earlier repair was not executed efficiently, blistering of the gel coat might result when the air bubbles expand. These dry blisters can be made good relatively easily by removing them with a tool such as bradawl and then renewing the gel coat in the same way as if it had been scored.

Wicking

Another laying-up fault, either during manufacture or repair, is to allow the fibres of glass from the first mat to penetrate the gel coat. This can lead to the ingress of water by capillary action. Once under the gel coat, this water might manifest itself as 'wet' bubbles or, worse still, it might break the bond between glass and resin, resulting in a serious loss of strength over the affected area. The bubbles can be dealt with as air bubbles, except that it will be necessary to remove all traces of salt and allow the surface to dry completely before attempting to apply a new gel coat. If the bubbles are extensive, it is probable that sufficient strength has been lost to justify removing the gel coat completely and then digging as deep as is necessary to get to good solid glass and resin. The extent and depth of the excavation will determine the type of repair required. The chances of wicking occurring can be minimised by the use of a surfacing tissue between the gel coat and the first glass mat. This is not a common practice among manufacturers.

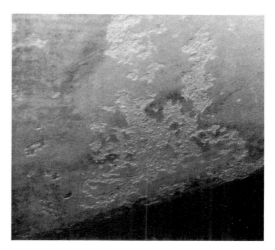

Cracks

Apart from by impact, cracks can be caused by over-tightening through-the-hull fastenings of fittings. The fastenings and fittings will have to be removed and the gel coat treated as for other cracks.

Osmosis

If a semi-permeable membrane is situated such that one side is in contact with a salt solution and the other is in contact with a salt solution of a different concentration, the weaker solution will pass through the membrane. That is a formal definition of osmosis. Contrary to earlier beliefs, a gel coat is not waterproof. It is a semi-permeable membrane.

The solvents and other chemical compounds inevitably present inside the gel coat form a strong salt solution. If, as is often the case, a hull is immersed in sea water, this takes on the role of the weaker salt solution and it will pass through the gel coat. If the hull were immersed in fresh water, an even weaker salt solution, the effect would be greater still.

Fortunately, the actual rate at which water passes through the gel coat is very slow, but it does increase with temperature. Thus, the problem is of greater prevalence in fresh water and also warmer tropical waters. Until such time as the chemistry of GRP construction has been changed, presumably in such a way that the residual solution inside the gel coat is of minimal salt content, osmosis will continue to be of long-term interest to the owners of GRP hulls.

Once water is inside the gel coat, it will spread by capillary action and eventually manifest itself in the form of 'wet' blisters. It is common that blisters caused by osmosis will be more extensive than those of other sources, probably, but not necessarily, covering the whole of the boat's bottom.

Whatever the cause of extensive blistering, the solution is always the same – remove all the affected gel coat, remove all traces of salt, allow to dry thoroughly, probably, in good conditions, over a period of three months, and then paint the hull with an epoxy resin. The removal of the gel coat from larger boats will be best left to one of the (few) companies with appropriate blast cleaning equipment. To attempt it 'dry' would be to endanger the health not only of the 'operator' but all in the immediate vicinity. Though this suggestion takes it out of the realm of 'Do-it-Yourself', it is included partly out of interest and partly because it is possible that a smaller boat could be tackled at home, assuming the right safety precautions are taken.

A suggestion which is becoming more and more common is that GRP hulls should be painted with epoxy resin from new. This would give improved resistance to osmosis for about five years.

Repairs

Tools

Provided the irritant value of the dust and the brittleness of the gel coat is borne in mind, GRP can be filed, drilled and sawn in much the same manner as other materials. Metal-working tools rather than wood-working are preferable, particularly for sawing.

Materials

Depending on the type of repair to be undertaken, some or all of the following will be needed:

Polyester resin and hardener – mix as indicated by the manufacturer.
Gel coat (resin mixed with a pigment) and hardener – you might have to mix your own colour.
Surfacing tissue, woven roving and chopped strand mat.
Glass-fibre paste – available commercially or made by mixing ⅛–¼ in (3–5mm) lengths of glass-fibres with resin.
Release agent – a wax polish or polyvinyl alcohol (PVA).
Cellophane – Mellamex?
Adhesive PVC tape – Sellotape?
Degreasing solvent – available from paint suppliers.
Wet and dry silicon carbide paper and sanding blocks.
Cutting polish – T-Cut?
Abrasive bath cleaner – Jif?
GRP polish.
Domestic detergent.
Disposable paint brushes – 1 and 2in (25 and 50mm).
Plastic containers for mixing the resin.
Modelling clay.

Technique

Gel coat Applied either from the 'inside' directly on to a mould or former treated with a release agent, or from the 'outside' on to the laminated glass and resin and then covered with cellophane or Sellotape. Unlike ordinary resin, gel coat will only cure completely if air is excluded from its surface. It must be mixed with hardener and then applied by brush, paying particular attention

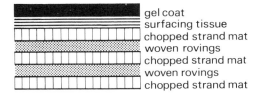

gel coat
surfacing tissue
chopped strand mat
woven rovings
chopped strand mat
woven rovings
chopped strand mat

to the corners. Apply a second coat when the first has cured sufficiently to still take an impression of the finger, but not to stick to it. When large areas are applied, shrinkage might take place, in which case the gaps will have to be filled with more gel coat – a sliver of wood can be used to apply such small quantities.

Mats That nearest the gel coat should be of surfacing tissue; subsequent laminations should alternate between chopped strand mat and woven rovings, in that order. Apply a generous coat of mixed resin and hardener over the whole surface, then stick the mat to it. Over-brush with more resin and stipple it well into the mat; work any bubbles to the edge. When adequately wetted, the mat will become translucent. White patches indicate dry areas. Subsequent layers are added while the resin is still wet. If resin is allowed to harden for more than about twenty-four hours, it will be necessary to rough up the surface with 300 grade dry paper before applying more. When overlapping mats or holes, aim for about 2in (50mm) – that is, the length of the strands of fibre in chopped strand mat.

Resin Always mixed with hardener as instructed by the manufacturer. On average, chopped strand mat needs 3 times its own weight in resin to give adequate wetting; alternate layers of chopped strand mat and woven rovings need about 1½ times. The working time of resin can be adjusted within limits by varying the amount of hardener used – initially it is best to aim for about 30–45 minutes and under-estimate the quantity of resin needed. In normal conditions, the recommended proportion of hardener to resin is 2 per cent. A proportion of less than 1 per cent will not allow for a complete cure, so never use less than half that recommended. Resin which is 'workable' for about ½ hour will be hard enough to rub down with sandpaper after about 4 hours, but it will be 24 hours before it is really hard. The final advice in this section is never to build up a mat thickness of more than about ¼ in (5mm) without allowing a cooling period, otherwise the overheating will seriously weaken the laminate.

Wet and dry silicone carbide paper When used wet, a little detergent in the water helps lubrication. Always be aware of the thickness of the gel coat – the manufacturer will have applied a maximum of about $\frac{1}{50}$ in

(½ mm). When it is getting thin, grey patches show through the surface. When rubbing down a gel coat to get a smooth finish, always use a block of cork or balsa wood.

Release agent It is essential to apply one to any surface on which the resin is not welcome. Either wax polish or PVA can be used to mask the surface surrounding the area to be repaired. Always use a release agent on a mould or former. For maximum effect, apply four coats of wax. PVA will take about 30 minutes to dry and can be removed with water.

Surface Abrasions

General oil and grease stains and the sort of scuff marks associated with gentle impacts and dirty fenders can be removed by one of four progressive techniques:

1 Wash with domestic detergent and warm water.
2 Rub with a mild 'bath' cleaner.
3 Polish with a paint-cutting polish.
4 Rub with 400 grade wet and dry used wet on a block; when the mark has been removed, improve the surface by rubbing

with 600 and then 1,000 grade wet and dry used wet on a block; polish with a paint-cutting polish; finish with a proprietary gel coat polish.

If, in the process of removing a surface abrasion, too much energy leads to too little gel coat – that is, when the darker under layers begin to show through – the remedy is to move on to another stage of repair which involves the removal of the gel coat.

Hairline Cracks

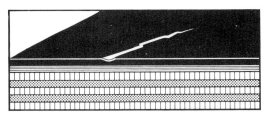

Though these cracks have not breached the gel coat, they should be dealt with promptly before the problem worsens.

crack sufficiently to see the first glass-fibres. Undercut the edges of the gel coat to about 45°. Remove all dust and particles using a brush – the oil film resulting from use of fingers will create a dark line around the finished repair. Mix the gel coat and perhaps a little less hardener than recommended. In small quantities of gel coat, overaction of the hardener might cause air bubbles and ruin the repair.

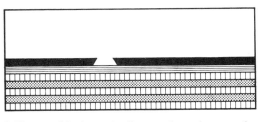

1 Use a chisel or similar tool to deepen the

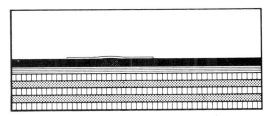

2 Press the gel well into the crack with a sliver of wood, overfilling a little so that it

stands proud. Stick a strip or strips of PVC adhesive tape over the whole repair – the gel coat will not harden if it is exposed to air – and roll a pencil over it to minimise the rubbing down.

3 When the gel coat has hardened completely (about four hours at 70°F (20°C)), remove the tape. Finish the repair as for step 4 of surface abrasions. If the colour match is good, and achieving that might well prove to be the most difficult part, the repair should be virtually invisible.

Scores and Grazes

These are thought of as being similar to hairline cracks in that the gel coat has not been breached, but the area affected is more extensive.

Remove all the affected gel coat and expose the glass-fibres, undercutting the edges to an angle of about 45°. Remove all the dust and particles. Overfill the whole area with mixed gel coat and hardener, then cover it with PVC tape or cellophane. With a squeegee, force out all the air bubbles

and fair off the repair.

When the gel coat has hardened, finish off as for a surface abrasion.

Mat Fractures

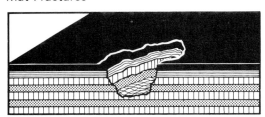

When the damage extends to the glass-fibre laminates, all the damaged mat and resin must be removed, even if that means making a hole right through the hull. The following assumes that to have been the case. If you have been lucky and still have laminations left, use the same technique but omit the patch inside the hull. Note that this repair has little structural strength.

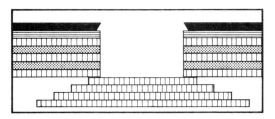

Remove all the damaged and loose resin and laminate. Shape the edges of the hole with a fine file or glass paper. With 300 grade wet and dry paper used dry, rough up the gel coat for about 1in (25mm) all round the hole. Undercut the gel coat to an angle of about 45°. On the inside, rough up the surface for about 4in (100mm) all round.

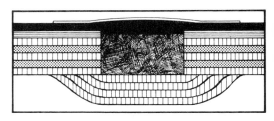

Cut four sheets of chopped strand mat, each to overlap the hole on the inside by 1, 1½, 2, and 3in (25, 40, 50 and 75mm) respectively. Mix enough resin and hardener to lay up these four mats, then do so symmetrically around the hole, starting with the smallest nearest the hull and progressing to the largest.

When the patch has hardened, pack the hole with glass-fibre paste to within ⅛in (3mm) of the surface and when that has hardened, finish the gel coat as for the earlier repairs, ensuring that all the roughed-up surface is covered.

An alternative method, if it is not convenient to get inside the hull, is as follows.

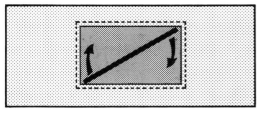

Enlarge the hole to a rectangle in order that a plywood pad, large enough to cover the hole completely can be passed through it on the diagonal. Drill two holes near the

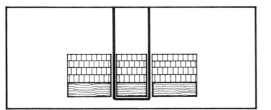

centre of the pad.

Lay up four layers of chopped strand mat on to the pad and while the resin is still wet, pass a length of wire through the holes in the pad and the laminates so that the ends of the wire are on the same side as the laminates. (An alternative to laying up the mats is to use a paste.) While the resin is still wet, pass the

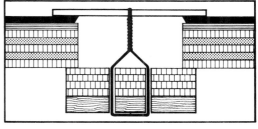

pad through the hole, position it symmetrically and apply a tourniquet via the wire to compress the laminates between the pad and the hull while the resin hardens.

Nip off the wires as close to the pad as possible, pack with glass-fibre paste and continue as for the previous repair.

Hull Punctures

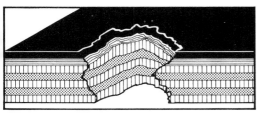

The foregoing repair methods will not contribute any structural strength to the hull. If the hull has been holed completely and any repair must be of structural strength, it will have to be laminated in a manner very similar to that employed when the hull was built. For this you must have access to the inside of the hull around the damaged area and fittings will have to be removed as necessary. The former used as a mould could be either Formica polished with a wax or plywood covered with cellophane.

Remove all the damaged and loose resin and mat. File the edges from both inside and out to an angle of about 60° so that the edge is in the shape of a V with the widest parts of the hole being at both surfaces. Inside,

rough up the surface for 4in (100mm) all round the hole with 300 grade paper used dry.

Fasten a former over the hole with through-the-hull bolts which are clear of the

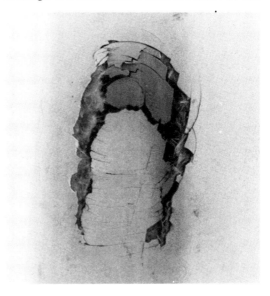

Hulls

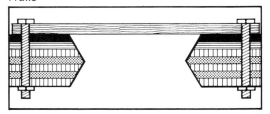

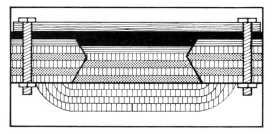

roughed-up area. Cut all the mat required, making the fit as close as possible: one surface tissue, as many chopped strand mats and woven rovings as will be necessary to fill the hole with alternate layers of each, four back-up laminates of chopped strand mat 1, 1½, 2 and 3in (25, 40, 55 and 75mm) larger than the hole respectively. Mix enough gel coat and hardener for one generous coat and brush it on to the inside face of the former, paying particular attention to the corners. Mix another similar quantity and when the first is of a similar texture to that of soft leather, apply a second coat. Mix enough

resin and hardener to lay up all the laminates, including the back-ups. As soon as the second gel coat texture is as already described, lay up all the mats, starting with the surfacing tissue, then alternate layers of chopped strand mat and woven rovings, in that order, until the inner surface is flush. While the resin is still wet, carry straight on with the back-up laminates – smallest against the hull. Leave all that to cure overnight.

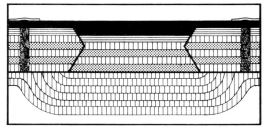

Remove the former and its bolts, then fill the bolt holes with glass-fibre paste so that the inner surface is flush and the outer will leave enough room for about ¼in (3mm) of gel coat. When the paste is hard, lay up two more laminations of chopped strand mat on the inside, the first overlapping the repair, including bolt holes, by 2in (50mm), the second by 4in (100mm). Fill the bolt holes and any other gaps with gel coat; cover it with PVC tape. When it has hardened, finish off the repair as for the earlier ones.

Making a Mould

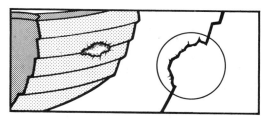

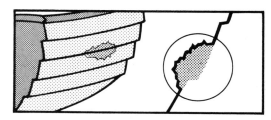

If the damage is on a part of the hull with curves which even a flexible former will not take up, it will be necessary to lay up a mould which can be used instead.

Before removing any of the damaged parts, push them into the original shape, or as near as can be achieved by hand and eye. Fill the remaining imperfections with modelling clay and make it as smooth as possible.

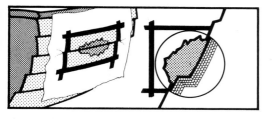

Mask off the area surrounding the damage, allowing about 6in (150mm) all round as working space.

Spray or brush PVA on to the whole area inside the masking. (If you use cellophane and scissors, the result will be a gel coat surface with irregularities which will have to be removed by filling and/or rubbing down.) Allow half an hour for the PVA to dry, apply a coat of resin, then lay up four or five layers of chopped strand mat, making sure that it is pushed well into any corners. When the mould has hardened, remove it from the hull. Wash off all the PVA with water. Any irregularities in the mould should be filled with resin and/or sanded to a smooth finish. Apply a release agent to the mould, then you are ready to proceed as for the previous repair.

Fixing through the Hull

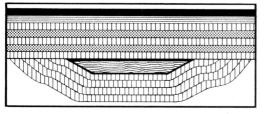

If any bolts or other fastenings are to be secured through the hull it is best to bond a strong-back to the inside in order that the load is spread as much as possible. The strong-back, probably made of wood, should have fully chamfered edges to allow for maximum contact of the bonding laminates. Bed the strong-back on to resin paste and apply four layers of chopped strand mat, the first overlapping the strong-back by 2in (50mm), the other three progressively larger by 1in (25mm) each.

If a strong-back is not used, washers of at least 2½ times the diameter of the fastening should be used under both head and nut.

Finally, whenever GRP is cut or drilled, the edges should be coated with resin to seal the ends of the glass-fibres and prevent wicking.

Foam Sandwich

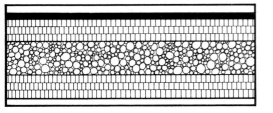

The sandwich is a layer of semi-rigid PVC foam, both sides of which are laminated with glass-fibre mat and resin. It is a method of construction which best lends itself to 'one off' designs. A wooden framework mould is made to the shape of the required hull, panels of foam are fastened to it and then the layers of mat and resin are added. The 'open sandwich' is removed from the mould and the inside glassed up. The final topside surface is a resin putty, applied with a plasterer's float, and then made good with a lot of elbow grease and glass paper.

All repairs to the laminations can be executed in the same way as for a moulded hull. The topside surface can be repaired either with gel coat or putty. If the foam has been damaged to the point where it needs replacing, any gaps remaining around the renewed foam can be filled with glass-fibre paste.

Preparation for Painting

The release agent applied to the original mould during the manufacture of the hull is likely to be present, even if unnoticed, for many years after launching. Before attempting to apply any paint, this, and any other dirt or grease deposits, must be removed. It is best to use one of the proprietary brands of degreasing solvents and follow the instructions.

Assuming that the degreasing has been carried out meticulously, no further treatment should be necessary. However, it is human to err and it is probable that there will be areas that are not as free of grease as they ought to be. To cover this eventuality, it would be as well to rub down the whole of the surface to be painted with about 300 grade wet and dry paper used wet. The object should be to achieve an overall matt finish. The critical test is to apply clean fresh water to the 'finished' hull. If it stays in a continuous sheet, the surface is indeed finished. If the water separates into globules, more work is necessary. When the surface is finished, it should be washed down with clean fresh water and allowed to dry.

STEEL

Construction

The type of steel most commonly used for boat construction is that known as 'mild' steel. The plates which are used to make up the hull are usually not less than ⅛in (3mm) thick because, though the steel is theoretically strong enough to be used thinner than that for small boats, it would dent and bend too easily. So, below a critical size, it is accepted that steel is too heavy. The hull plates are continuously welded edge to edge, and those on the outside are ground flush to give a smooth finish. Those on the inside are usually only ground off if they will be seen. The design may or may not call for frames. If they are used, the plates are usually welded to them intermittently rather than with a continuous weld.

Two big advantages of a steel hull are its great strength and, almost guaranteed, watertightness – that is, if it was welded properly during construction. A third, and not insignificant advantage, is the extra space below decks created by the thin hull plates and often complete absence of frames. No frames also means easier below-decks maintenance.

Of course, there are some disadvantages and one is the effect of the steel on a magnetic compass. Structurally, a disadvantage is that due to the relative positions of steel and lead in the electro-chemical series; if the latter is used as a ballast keel, it must be insulated from the hull to prevent the steel from being eaten away. Similarly, if lead is used as internal ballast it must also be insulated. This can be achieved by setting it in concrete but, hopefully, the original builder will have attended to these problems.

Faults

Assuming that the original construction, particularly the welding, was good, the hull should be completely watertight, and the only faults which can occur are those caused by corrosion or impact damage. Even as a result of quite heavy impacts the damage will

often be just a dent. It will have been a serious event indeed if the hull was holed completely.

Corrosion

Creation of the oxide, otherwise known as rust, on the surface of mild steel is brought about by an electro-chemical reaction. The composition of mild steel is such that areas of differing electrical potential exist. If a plate of mild steel is immersed in water, an electric current will flow from an area of high electrical potential via the electrolyte (water) to an area of relatively low electrical potential. If, while this electric current is flowing, oxygen is also present, the oxide (rust) will form where the current leaves the metal and enters the water. Since the composition of mild steel is what it is, the only way in which we can influence the formation of the rust is to control one or both of the other two requirements, water and oxygen. A perfectly sound coat of good paint, well adhered to the metal, will prevent rusting by excluding the water and air, the source of oxygen.

Rust manifests itself as a volume up to fifty times that of the metal which has been used in its production. The effect of this is twofold. Rust always looks a good deal worse than it really is and will lift any paint on top of it, causing it to crack. The second of these two effects allows more water and oxygen to the steel, so the problem gets progressively worse. The only cure is to remove meticulously every trace of rust and apply a sound coat of paint. How this is best achieved is discussed later as part of the section Preparation for Painting.

Repairs

The obvious way to effect repairs on a steel hull is by welding. The necessary equipment is relatively cumbersome and expensive and requires training and practice to attain proficiency. Though I am happy to accept that a large number of owners of steel hulls have acquired both the equipment and the expertise to use it, for the above mentioned reasons, I am considering welding as being beyond the scope of this book.

My proposition is that the best DIY repairs can probably be made using GRP techniques and I refer you to that section for details of the materials required.

Dents

All of the damaged area and about 2in (50mm) all round it must be taken back to bare metal, removing all traces of rust and

paint, finishing with a roughed-up surface. This can be done with a grinder, a wire brush or coarse glass paper used dry. When that preparation is complete, mix hardener with glass-fibre paste and fill the dent. When the paste has hardened, sand it smooth. Mix hardener and resin and fill any remaining irregularities. Once again, sand this until it is smooth and apply a priming paint immediately.

Holes

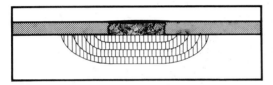

The first thing to do is cut four pieces of chopped strand mat. One will overlap the

hole by 1in (25mm) all round, and the others by 1½, 2 and 2¾in (40, 55 and 70mm) respectively. On the inside of the hull, take the surface for 4in (100mm) round the hole back to roughed-up metal. Mix the resin and hardener and lay up the four patches of chopped strand mat over the hole. Start with the smallest and progress to the largest. Complete the repair as though it were a dent.

Preparation for Painting

For a paint film to be of maximum use, it must adhere to the steel and not to any intervening surface such as rust. The process of manufacturing mild steel results in a skin of iron oxide on the surface. This is the mill scale. So, if you are contemplating painting a steel hull, whether it is old and a little rusty or new and covered in mill scale, the surface will have to be taken back to bare, rough metal. For this preparation, there are several methods available, each with its own degree of effectiveness.

Hand Tools Wire brushes, scrapers and chipping hammers are of limited use. They might make the operator feel as though a lot is being achieved, but none of these tools will remove corrosion from the bottom of the pits.

Power Tools Wire brushes and sanders operated by power enable the limited effect of hand tools to be achieved quicker. They will also polish corrosion and metal alike which, if nothing else, gives the poor job a nice appearance. Abrasive discs will certainly cut through corrosion, just as in careless hands it will the metal, but, once again, it will not get to the bottom of the pits. An air-operated needle gun is quite good at removing corrosion from pits, but will also polish the surface. It is also a slow and noisy process.

Blast Cleaning This consists of blasting the hull with abrasive grit at high pressure. The equipment will probably have to be hired, as might also be an experienced operator. In this respect it is not DIY, but the process is

50

ST. BUDEAUX

so superior to any other, it must be worth considering, certainly if you want to paint a complete hull. Freshly blasted areas should be cleared of dust with a stiff brush and a priming coat applied within two hours. To achieve this, it will probably be necessary to alternate side to side, blasting and painting. But do make sure that no dust settles on the paint until it is hard enough to be brushed clean.

ALUMINIUM

Construction

In its pure form, aluminium is both light in weight and virtually immune to most forms of corrosion found in a marine environment. Unfortunately, it is also both soft and not strong enough for general constructional use. By the addition of suitable alloying elements such as copper, magnesium and silicon, its strength can be increased while still retaining the basic advantages of being light and resistant to sea water corrosion. A number of these alloys is used in the construction of boats and because one of the few problems with aluminium is a susceptibility to galvanic action, it is important to appreciate that this is so. Great care must be taken to ensure that all repairs are completed using a similar or compatible material to that with which the boat was originally constructed.

The plates of which aluminium boats are made may be joined by either welding or riveting.

Because of its low melting point, 600°C as opposed to 1,400°C for steel, the welding of aluminium is generally regarded as difficult. A further liability in this context is that it melts with no change of colour to give a warning. For those reasons it will be assumed that any joining of plates will be effected by cold riveting. Being a soft material, rivets of up to about ½in (12mm) in diameter can be hammered cold. Those larger need to be heated to a temperature of between 400 and 500°C, presenting another temperature control problem not easily solved by the amateur.

Faults

Aluminium itself has few faults. Its high resistance to corrosion apparently makes it an ideal material with which to build a boat. Unfortunately, it is a metal which is less noble than almost any other commonly used in the construction of boats and their fittings. Consequently, a lot of care must be taken in the selection and fitting of any

equipment. Zinc and cadmium are quite close in the electro-chemical series, which means that galvanised rowlock sockets are satisfactory, for instance. Stainless steel and yellow metals can never be used safely. If any fittings other than galvanised or cadmium plated are used, they should be bedded on an insulator, such as a plastic or tufnol washer.

One of the apparent faults of aluminium is that the shiny new metal rapidly oxidises and takes on a dull finish. Not only that, if you rub your fingers along it they will be blackened, as will clothes and sails which rub against it. Though the hull will last inde-

finitely with this oxidised surface, which actually protects it from further corrosion, most would prefer to have a clean boat. This can be achieved and maintained by frequent washing with a strong detergent and fresh water and then polishing. Best results will be obtained by using a polish intended specifically to be used on aluminium. The alternative is to paint the hull.

In time, some of the rivets might work loose, particularly so if the hull has been strained, and this will probably result in a leak. The cure is to 'harden' the rivets using the technique described under Riveting.

The only other likely faults will be caused by impacts and will fall into one or more of three categories: dents, cracks and holes. Because of the low melting point of aluminium and the associated fine temperature control necessary for welding and hot riveting, cold riveting is the only way of joining sections which will be considered.

Finally, I will repeat an earlier warning. Do make sure that all patches and rivets used are either of the same or a compatible material to that of the hull. If there is any doubt at all it is worth contacting the original manufacturer to find out which particular alloy he used.

Repairs

Riveting

When deciding the size and spacing of rivets for repairs, be guided by the manufacturer, but remember two things: (1) ½in (12mm) diameter is the limit for cold hammering; (2) the rivets used, and any plate for that matter, must be of a similar or compatible alloy to that used for the rest of the hull.

Rivets may be round headed or countersunk. Apart from being neater, the latter can produce a better watertight joint, but you do need sufficient plate thickness for the countersinking. Again, take your guidance from the manufacturer. The diameter of the rivet should be twice the total thickness of the plates through which it will pass, and the hole through which it will do that should be a tight fit.

Given enough room on the inside for the hammering, the rivet should be pressed home from the outside and bedded in mastic or an epoxy resin. The correct length of shank protruding through is 1–1¼ times the diameter for countersinking and 1½–2 times for round heads.

A dolly, of necessity significantly heavier than the hammer to be used, is offered up to the head of the rivet. Ideally, for countersunk rivets it will have the same head size or,

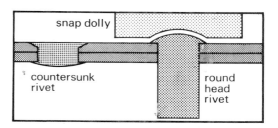

snap dolly

countersunk rivet

round head rivet

for round heads, it will be a 'snap' dolly, that is, one with a hollow recess to match the head shape. In the absence of such refinements, the head of whatever dolly is available should be covered with a few layers of masking tape to minimise damage to the heads and hull.

On the inside, take a ball pein hammer and use the flat head to 'start' the rivet and finish the shaping with the ball pein, using a series of short, sharp blows. When hardening rivets, take the trouble to do a few either side of the obvious faulty ones; it will save effort in the long term.

Finally, even though it might seem possible, resist the temptation to rivet single-handed. Two people working together nearly always produce a better result.

Dents

Small dents can be removed by holding a heavy dolly, preferably contoured to a shape something like the intended shape of the hull, on the 'high' side of the dent, while hitting the other side with a rubber mallet. Once again, it might prove useful to cover the dolly with tape to protect the hull. The impact which caused the dent will have stretched the metal and the object of the hammering is to shrink it to as near its original size as possible. This is best achieved by starting the hammering outside of the damage and working around it in ever decreasing circles towards the centre. Make sure you always hammer against the dolly or the problem will be compounded.

This technique has two snags associated with it: it requires a lot of practice to become proficient and with repeated hammering the aluminium 'work hardens', making the task progressively more difficult. The first should be taken as a warning, for it will be overcome only with time and patience. The second might be overcome by doing the same as the professional, that is, to anneal or soften the metal by applying heat from a gas torch. But remember the low melting point of aluminium and the fact that it melts with no forewarning of colour change. If you have some spare plate with which to experiment, you could try rubbing soap on to it before applying the heat. With some soap and some alloys, the soap will turn black at the required temperature. However, the first time you try applying the heat in earnest will probably result in a blob of aluminium plopping out without warning. But do not despair, there follows advice on repairing a hole.

Cracks

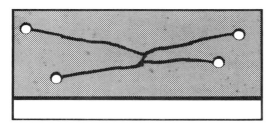

Though not very common, cracks can occur and are best repaired as follows. First, it is essential to drill small holes at the ends of each crack to stop them getting any longer. Second, from a sheet of compatible aluminium, cut with snips or saw with a hacksaw a patch of such a size that when it is in position no part of the cracks will be within 1in (25mm) of the edge.

Rivets, the diameter of which will be twice the combined thickness of patch and hull, will be set 1½ times that diameter in from the edge of the patch and spaced at intervals of 3 times that diameter if the repair is at or near the water line, otherwise at intervals of 5 times that diameter. If possible, drill all the holes through the patch and the hull together to guarantee that they line up. If that is not possible, drill the minimum necessary to secure temporarily the patch with nuts and bolts and then drill the remaining holes through both patch and hull together.

When all the holes have been drilled, and countersunk if required, remove all traces of burr from the holes and edges so that the patch and hull will marry up properly. Before starting the riveting, bed the patch on mastic or epoxy resin, securing it in place with a few nuts and bolts. To minimise the chances of the patch stretching and putting the holes out of alignment, first put in every sixth rivet, not forgetting to bed them in something. Finally, remove the nuts and bolts and complete the riveting. Whether the patch is fitted inside or outside the hull will be decided by both aesthetics and practicalities.

Holes

It will probably have taken a fairly hard impact from an unfriendly pointed object to pierce the hull completely, but if that is the case, it can be repaired with a patch. The first step is to enlarge the hole to a regular shape, probably a rectangle, and then cut a patch of compatible aluminium to fit it

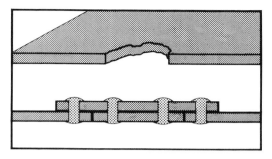

exactly. A second patch, 4in (100mm) larger all round than the enlarged hole is then bedded on mastic or epoxy resin and riveted in place. The last step is to offer up the first patch to the hole and rivet it to the patch which is already in position. The spacing of rivets for both patches should follow the same guidelines as previously stated. If sufficient care was taken when enlarging the hole and cutting its matching patch, the result should be quite a neat repair.

An even stronger repair can be effected by simply tidying up the damage and then riveting two identical patches, one either side of the hull. For this repair you will need slightly larger rivets.

Preparation for Painting

The method of preparing the surface of aluminium for painting can equally well be used for the preparation of galvanised steel. As with all metal surfaces, the objective is a thorough degreasing in order that the paint will have a decent chance of adhering. First, the complete hull, or whatever, should be rubbed down lightly with 600 grade paper used dry to remove any hard wax, grease or dirt. Then apply copious quantities of white spirit or a commercial degreasing solvent backed up with plenty of elbow-grease and clean cloths. Finally, remove all traces of abrasives, grease, cleaner etc, with a fresh water hose and allow the surface to dry.

FERRO-CEMENT

Construction

Ferro-cement hulls are made of reinforced cement (as opposed to reinforced concrete). The reinforcing often takes the form of a framework of mild steel rods tied together with wire, to which is attached three or four layers of wire mesh on each side. The mesh is usually in the form of galvanised chicken wire, not that the galvanising is necessary in the finished hull, for a bit of rust will help the adhesion of the mortar, but it might prevent the wire rusting away completely during construction. For maximum strength, the layers of mesh should be so tightly packed that the mortar can only just be forced through. The mortar mix of one part of ordinary Portland cement to two of fine, salt-free sand by weight, is so dense and waterproof that a layer of ⅛in (3mm) covering the wire is all that is normally required.

Faults

Ferro-cement suffers from none of the faults associated with other materials. It is virtually a permanent material; it will not rot or decay. It is not affected by ultra-violet light or marine borers. It will not rust and is fireproof. The biggest problem seems to be in attaining a good smooth finish to the hull. It is very strong and the result of impact damage will, nearly always, be just surface damage, though a piercing of the hull is a possibility.

Repairs

Surface Damage

All the loose and damaged mortar must be removed and the reinforcing pushed back into place. The mortar, mixed with good drinking water, must then be forced into every gap to completely fill the hole. The surface will be finished with a trowel to fair it in with the rest of the hull, but a smooth finish can be achieved by gently brushing with a water-soaked paint brush, the larger the better. The bond between old and new mortars will be improved if an epoxy bonding agent is applied to the old before plastering. Emergency repairs can be effected with a rapid setting mortar, but the shortage of plastering time will probably lead to a less than perfect finish.

Hull Puncture

If this is the problem, once again the first step is to remove all the loose and damaged mortar. It is probable that the mesh has been damaged and the torn pieces will have to be cut out. If the mild steel rods have been bent, they will have to be pushed back into shape, probably with a hydraulic jack. When the rods are in the right shape, it might be necessary to chip away more mortar to bare enough of the sound mesh to bind new sections to it, using wire ties. The mortar should be forced through from the inside, skimming off the surplus from the outside until the hole is absolutely full. The inside and outside is then finished as before.

Preparation for Painting

Once the mortar has set, it can be rubbed down with a medium grade carborundum stone or 180 grade paper on a block, in either case lubricated with copious quantities of fresh water. Keep the elbows going until the hull is as smooth and fair as you want it! Before welcoming paint, new mortar likes to be completely dry and fully cured. This can take up to a month.

INFLATABLES

The only inflatables to be considered are those which are used as boats in their own right or those used as tenders. Liferafts have a special purpose and should be serviced by specialists in the interest of saving life. Information on repairing them while they are in use is included in the general survival instructions.

Faults

Abrasions, often caused by thoughtlessly dragging the boat up a beach or along a quay, can wear holes in the bottom or the inflated tubes. Pointed objects can pierce the skin. Leaving the dinghy badly folded, perhaps during a long winter, can cause cracks. In all cases, if the puncture or tear is near a reinforcing strip or on the transom where it might be necessary to take the weight and thrust off an outboard motor, it would be as well to entrust the repair to a professional.

Repairs

Small air leaks from an inflated section can be found by spreading detergent over the suspect area. Bubbles will identify the leak. Wipe away the detergent and mark the spot with an indelible pencil. Deflate the dinghy and set the repair area up on a flat surface.

Puncture

Select, or from suitable material cut, a patch of such a size that its edges will be at least 1in (25mm) from the puncture. Offer up the patch and mark around it. Rough up the marked area with fine paper or emery cloth. Spread a thin layer of adhesive evenly over the marked area and when it has dried spread a second coat and another on to the patch. When this second coat is tacky, press the patch into place, cover it with French chalk and apply weight to the patch. Leave it for 24 hours.

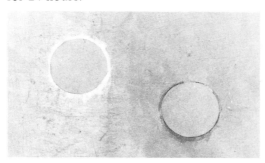

Tear

A tear or crack of significant length, say, of more than 1in (25mm), should be sewn with a herring-bone stitch before patching. This will hold the edges together without allowing them to overlap. When spreading the adhesive, ensure that none finds its way through the tear to form an unwanted adhesion.

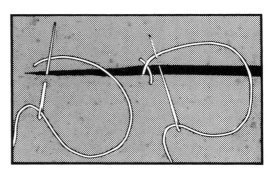

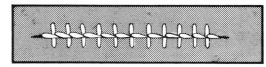

6 Painting and Varnishing

There is no short cut to an immaculate finished coat of paint. A good start is made by choosing the materials carefully. That means more than just picking the right colour of paint. It means selecting paints to serve the purpose you have in mind. It means having thinners appropriate to those paints. You must decide when the job can be improved by the use of mechanical aids and when a bad job can be hastened by their use. You must have the right grade of abrasive paper and the energy to use it. Finally, of course, you must really want an immaculate finish.

Materials

Apart from the paint itself, there are a few other expendable items involved in the application of paint.

Paint

Today's paint manufacturers produce what is, at first sight at least, a bewildering selection of paints and varnishes. So good is it, in fact, that you will be most unlikely to have a requirement which cannot be suited precisely. How do you want to apply it? Do you need rapid drying? Do you want a hard finish on the bottom? Will you be sailing in fresh or salt water?

Broadly speaking, there are five types of paint, each with a specific purpose described by its name: primer, undercoat, top coat, antifoul and varnish. Within each type there is a choice of chemical make-up which imparts various diverse qualities within its basic type.

Primers are those paints first applied to a surface, providing a key for subsequent coats. Some will seal a porous surface, some will etch a metal surface. The choice of primer will be determined by three factors: (1) the type of surface to be painted; (2)

whether or not that surface will be under water; (3) the paint to be applied subsequently.

Undercoats are usually quite opaque and form the basis of the final colour. When set, the paint is relatively soft, allowing it to be rubbed smooth before applying a top coat. The choice is determined by the type of top coat and the colour of the top coat.

Top coats supply the finish. They are often glossy, but a selection of matt finishes is available. To minimise the effect of brush marks on the final surface, these top coats are fairly thin and as a result are not very effective at covering other colours. Which chemical type is used will be strongly influenced by the surface to be painted. For example, a clinker-built boat which works and needs some water between its planks to become watertight needs a slightly porous paint. An epoxide or polyurethane with a much higher waterproofing ability would be quite unsuitable. So the type used will be determined by the surface to be painted and colour.

Antifoul paint is quite different from all other paints. Normally applied to below-water sections, its most significant ingredient is a poison which will kill one or more types of marine organisms. Generally, there are two ways in which the poison is released. 'Soft' antifoul paint slowly dissolves in the water, maintaining a solution of poison around the hull until all the paint has been used. 'Hard' antifoul paints work in a different way. Water permeates the skin of the paint and extracts the poison with no obvious effect on the paint itself. The surface can look as good at the end of the season as it did at the beginning, even if it has no antifouling property remaining. The poison most commonly used is based on copper. This being an expensive constituent, various strengths are produced to suit different

localities, allowing the user to pay only for the degree of protection he needs. Other non-metallic poisons are used to obviate electrolytic problems with metal hulls.

Varnish is basically a paint without pigments and is used to protect wood without obscuring its natural features. The equivalents of primers and undercoats are made by diluting it with suitable thinners. As with paint top coats, it is available with gloss or a selection of matt finishes, which might also be either porous or completely waterproof. The decision as to which is used will be influenced by the type of wood and the surface finish required.

Thinners

Along with each paint you finally select, you will need an appropriate thinning agent. It will serve two purposes: it can be mixed with the paint to vary its consistency; it is also used for cleaning the brushes or rollers, or whatever else you might use to apply the paint. For 'ordinary' paints white spirit might be the correct thinning agent, but this is not suitable for a large number of modern paints and antifoulings. The manufacturers of paint also produce the thinners and often identify them by a number. For example, International Thinners No 3 is intended for use with TBT antifouling; Blake's No 5 is intended for use with epoxy paints.

Paint Remover

A number of chemical paint removers are available. Some are water soluble, some are not; some are suited to the removal of one type of paint and not another. They are particularly suitable if the surface is to be varnished, where the scorched wood resulting from burning off the paint would be unsightly. Some are inflammable, others give off dangerous fumes, so read the label carefully. Normally, a liberal coat is brushed on to the paint and then left for a while. When the paint has erupted into blisters, it is removed with a scraper. If the paint is old or particularly thick, more than one application might be necessary. After use, the stripper must be neutralised in accordance with the manufacturer's instructions and every trace removed from the surface. You will probably find that any stopping present will have reacted with the stripper and become soft. It will have to be removed and then renewed after the first priming coat of paint has been applied. After stripping, any paint remaining in the grain can be removed by rubbing along it with 100 grade dry paper, and then finally smoothing the whole surface with 220 grade waterproof paper used dry, prior to painting.

Abrasives

Waterproof silicon carbide papers are available in grades from 60 to 1200 and may be used either wet or dry. Coarse dry glass paper is available in grades from 30 to 100, and is often in a variety of shapes and sizes to suit the various mechanical sanding devices.

Provided it is washed frequently to prevent the grit getting clogged, waterproof paper is more efficient when used wet. The addition of a little detergent to the water will help the lubrication. When rubbing down by hand, greater surface-to-surface contact will be made if the paper is backed up with a block of wood or cork and, consequently, the process will be quicker.

Stoppers

If the major stopping or hole filling was done at the repair stage, the most likely stopper to be used for the final preparation and painting will be a trowel cement. This is normally white, but is available in a selection of other colours to match the surface if it is to be varnished. Other stoppers are available as either a 'soft' variety for use between working planks, for instance, or a 'hard' variety for use as a filler where no movement is expected.

Equipment: Prior to Painting

At various stages in the preparation and painting of surfaces some equipment, perhaps a paint brush, can be considered as essential. Other items, such as mechanical sanders, though not essential, might be used to improve the finish, or at least to hasten progress towards it.

Scrapers

Scrapers are used to remove paint which has already been loosened by old age or the application of heat or a chemical. Flat scrapers have flexible blades, available in a selection of sizes. In use, they are intended to be pushed and this makes them unsuitable for use when burning off paint.

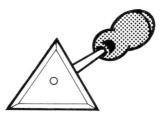

Triangular: suitable for flat surfaces and getting into corners.

General purpose: suitable for a selection of surfaces.

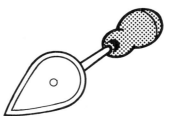

Curved: suitable for concave surfaces only.

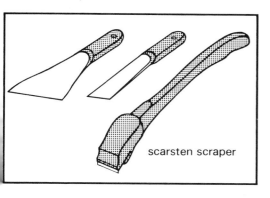

scarsten scraper

Scarsten scraper: can be fitted with a selection of blades of various profiles to suit most surfaces. The hot, sometimes flaming, paint is not usually welcome on the back of the hand. In fact, for most paint-removal jobs, those scrapers known as shave hooks, which are designed to be pulled, are of more use. They are available in a number of shapes and sizes:

When using a shave hook or scarsten scraper for dry scraping, its efficiency can be increased by exerting downward pressure with the other hand. This is not recommended if the scraper is also being heated.

Burners

Perhaps more accurately described as blow-lamps, these are used for paint removal. The heat produced melts the paint, allowing it to be scraped off easily. Most paints encountered on boats are suitable for burning off, though others, such as emulsion or cellulose, are not.

Before applying heat to any paint, there are a few things to be considered. Will the surface underneath the paint be damaged by the heat? Will the heat be conducted to another surface which might be damaged? Will the hot and burning paint fall where it might be dangerous? When making these considerations, think of the other side of the bulkhead and inspect there regularly, particularly at the end of the working day.

  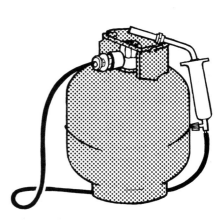

Paraffin blowlamps are the traditional burners but are difficult and messy to light.

Cartridge burners are convenient – easy to light and when the gas runs out you simply throw away the cylinder and screw the burner to a new one.

Blow torches attached to larger cylinders by a hose are the most economical if the area to be stripped of paint is large.

Right-handed people will find it best to hold the burner in the left hand, scraper in the right, and work from right to left and top to bottom. As the heat is applied the paint will soften and erupt in bubbles prior to bursting into flame. The best time to remove it is between bubbling and burning. With practice, while one area is being scraped, the next can be melted and a continuous motion developed. Take care to char the wood as little as possible and try not to gouge grooves in the hull. Particularly, do not touch the end of the scraper, which is probably just a little cooler than red heat. Finally, do keep an eye on where the flakes of paint are falling and on the other side of the surface on which you are working.

Mechanical Sanders

In the right hands, a mechanical sander can certainly minimise the amount of time necessary to rub down a surface. In the wrong hands it can also damage the wood to such an extent that the time taken to repair it can more than outweigh the time saved. For a given effect, it will be found that the grade of paper needed will be coarser than that which would have been used by hand. The faster the paper moves, the larger will be the grain size necessary to produce a given smoothness of surface. For safety's sake, only use high-voltage machinery when there is no danger of it making contact with water and, of course, use them for dry rubbing down only.

Whichever mechanical aid is used for sanding, it is inevitable that to obtain a good finish the last rub down must be by hand. Use a fine paper and a block.

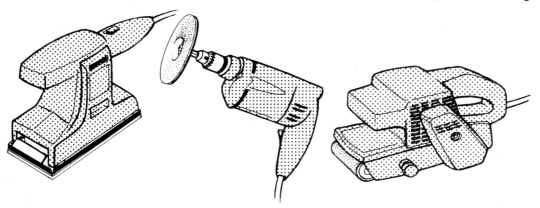

The orbital sander, probably because it is the kindest, is the type most commonly used on boats. If it has been used carefully, the surface can be perfected finally with a light rub down by hand with fine paper.

Disc sanders may have either a fixed or flexible head. The former is definitely not for the inexperienced. The flexible head can be very useful for removing large quantities of material, but the difference in speed between the centre and the edge of the disc is so great that it is easy to 'dig in' the edge and remove a relatively deep crescent shape from the surface. That will usually call for stopping and then even more rubbing down.

The belt sander is probably the most efficient for large flat surfaces. The speed of the paper is constant for the whole width, so the effect is fairly predictable. Apart from the expense of purchasing or hiring one, the biggest problem found will be the weight. When working down on to a horizontal surface the weight might prove to be advantageous, but for vertical surfaces like topsides it is not at all advantageous. If the bulk of the weight can be supported from above with a semi-elastic line, it is possible to bounce and swing the machine to cover a limited area without undue strain to the arms.

Painting Equipment

Though most painting of boats is done by brush, there might be occasions when rollers, sprays or pads can be used to advantage.

Brushes

Good preparation and selection of a good-quality paint can often be negated by choosing the wrong brush. Though it is quite easy to find brushes at 'throw away' prices, they do not always represent the best buy. A first-class brush, properly used and cared for will last indefinitely. If all the nooks and crannies are to be painted efficiently, a selection of sizes is essential. The largest will probably be between 4in and 6in (100mm and 150mm) and the smallest, only used for the minutest work, ½in (12mm).

The object of putting a brush into a pot of paint is to load it with paint, and this is best achieved by immersing it to a depth of ½–1in (12–25mm). A common mistake is to load the brush with too much paint and then remove the surplus by wiping the brush against the rim of the pot. This technique is bad for two reasons: it wastes time and it allows drying paint to accumulate on the rim, and flakes of this will eventually fall into the pot and end up on the newly painted surface. If you do get too much paint on the brush, the surplus is best removed by scraping it against a clean palette knife or something similar held over the pot.

When the brush has been loaded correctly, it should be held at right angles to the surface and the paint applied with both horizontal and vertical strokes until it is spread evenly. Finally, it should be 'laid off' with the brush held at an angle of about 45°. This will minimise the chances of residual brush marks. Right-handed painters normally work from right to left. This enables the left hand to be steadied on a dry surface.

The paint in the heel of the brush will dry gradually, even as the brush is being used, and the skin so formed will eventually find its way down the bristles, with fairly predictable results. The only cure for this complaint is to clean the brush frequently. If speedy application of the paint is essential, this minor chore can be postponed if more than one clean brush is available.

When the painting is finished, the brushes should be thoroughly washed with the appropriate thinners, changing the solvent as often as is necessary to remove all traces of paint or varnish. They should then be washed with warm water and detergent until a good froth is obtained, indicating that all the solvent has been removed. The detergent is then removed by rinsing thoroughly in more warm water. Finally, the hairs should be wrapped in greaseproof paper, as near as possible to the way in which the manufacturer wrapped the brush when new. Make sure that all the hairs are laid flat and none are bent back. If an elastic band is used to secure the paper, put it around the metal, not the bristles.

While in regular use, it might be more convenient to keep brushes in thinners between painting sessions. In this case it is best to have a 'keep' for each colour, using either a jam jar or something larger if more appropriate. The advantage of using a jar with a lid is that the brush handle can be fitted through the lid enabling a fairly airtight fit to reduce evaporation of the thinners. If a lid is

not available, the handle of the brush can be pushed through a square of kitchen foil and the edges of that tucked around the neck of the jar. There should be about 1in (25mm) between the bottom of the keep and the brush to keep the bristles out of any sediment, and the thinners should cover them completely. While the brushes are stored in this manner, the thinner will dissolve the paint from the bristles and the sediment will fall to the bottom. When required for use again, the surplus thinner is simply shaken out. To be fully effective, the keep should be cleaned regularly and the thinner renewed.

If polyurethane or antifoul paints have been used, they cannot be stored in a keep. The choice is either to clean them immediately or throw them away.

The storing of dirty brushes in water or linseed oil is one way of spoiling them, but that is neither as quick nor as effective as cleaning them with the wrong thinners.

Rollers

A roller consists of a handle supporting a spindle to which is fitted a sleeve – that part which holds the paint and rolls. The sleeve is usually available as a foam or lambswool and the price of each reflects the quality. The roller is of particular benefit when painting large areas free of obstructions, where a gloss finish is not required. An inclined tray a little wider than the roller is used to hold the paint reservoir. Naturally, the paint finds its way to the lower end of the tray and it is there that the roller is dipped into it, prior to being rolled up and down the ribbed 'dry' portion of the tray to distribute the paint evenly around the roller. The paint is then applied to the surface in arm-span rolls, criss-crossing as necessary to achieve an even coverage. Applying as it does bands of paint 8–11in (200–300mm) wide, it makes for fast painting. However, there is a speed limit, beyond which the paint is thrown off the roller in a myriad of globules, most of which seem to find a route on to the face of the user.

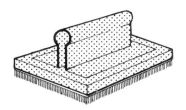

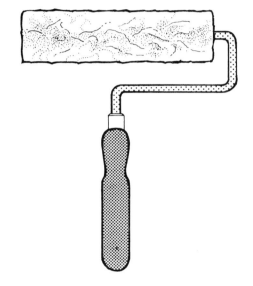

Rollers and trays can be cleaned and thus used time and time again, but for the cost involved, the foam sleeve might as well be thrown away. The rest, having been dismantled, can be cleaned with an appropriate thinner, washed in warm soapy water, rinsed in warm clean water and dried.

Pads

A paint pad consists of a handle, a backing plate, a layer of foam and a thin layer of mohair pile. It is used in conjunction with a flat tray which holds the paint reservoir. Just the pile is dipped into the paint and then the pad is simply drawn along the surface to be painted. The advantage of using a pad is that it is quicker than a brush and cleaner than a roller. The disadvantages are that it is rela-

tively tiring to use and the finish is not usually good enough for a final coat. Pads can be cleaned using thinners, soap and water.

Spray

In the right hands and with good rubbing down between coats, a spray gun enables a first-class gloss finish to be achieved. However, it can only be used successfully in still air, for the fine spray will travel a long way down-wind, perhaps to the detriment of someone else's hull.

It is essential to use paint of the correct viscosity and this is best achieved by buying a paint which has been mixed specifically for spraying or diluting a standard paint with thinners according to the recommendations of the manufacturer. The relatively thin paint inevitably means that each coat is proportionately thinner than those applied by other means. It is the necessary extra coats and the opportunity to rub down each with fine paper which allows for a first-class finish.

Practice is the only way to become proficient with a spray gun – preferably using a surface other than your boat. The distance which the gun should be held from the surface is critical and is determined by the type and pressure of the particular gun used. A typical distance is about a foot (300mm). This distance should be maintained for the whole of any one run, resisting the temptation to move the arm and gun in an arc.

This, of course, severely restricts the length of any one run.

To start, the gun should be pointed away from the surface to be painted and the spray switched on as the gun is swung into position, switching off as it is turned away at the end of the run. When correctly applied, each stripe will be feathered at each end and at the top and bottom. As subsequent stripes are added while the paint is still wet, the feathering should overlap sufficiently to make a coat of even thickness.

As with all other pieces of equipment involved in the application of paint, the spray gun should be thoroughly cleaned with thinners, paying particular attention to the nozzle.

Conditions

The best atmospheric conditions for painting and varnishing are when it is warm and dry, with a gentle breeze sufficiently strong to remove the solvent from the paint so that it will dry quickly, but not so strong that it stirs up dust or whips the paint from the brush. Dampness, even in the form of high humidity, must be avoided at all costs, and if there is any chance of an overnight frost, painting should be terminated early in the afternoon. In northern Europe it is rarely sensible to paint in the open air outside of the hours of 1000–1600. Another extreme, that of strong, hot sunshine should also be avoided – should that opportunity present itself! The enthusiastic owner can always take advantage of the rain to rub down with 'wet' wet and dry paper.

When the atmospheric conditions are right, the surface should be thoroughly cleaned to remove every sign of dust, dirt and grease. Use a vacuum cleaner for the bulk of the dust and then wipe over firmly with a clean cloth soaked in white spirit. The surface should then be allowed to dry completely.

When painting, wear non-fluffy, dust-free clothes (remember, it is supposed to be warm and dry).

Application: Wood

Above the Water Line: Carvel and Clinker
Old paint can be removed by either burning it off or using a chemical stripper. Burning is probably best if the surface is to be painted for any charring will soon be disguised, but if the surface is to be varnished, a chemical stripper is better. After burning off, any paint remaining in the grain can be removed with 100 grade dry sand paper, which should be rubbed along the grain. The final preparation of the bare wood, whether new or recently burnt off, is to rub down with 220 grade wet and dry paper used dry. The application of the paint now follows in three stages: priming; undercoat; top coat. If existing paint work is to be made good, join in at a later stage, probably for the rubbing down of the second undercoat. If an area of new wood is to be patched in, the adjoining good paint should be feathered to bare wood by rubbing down and then follow the full procedure, paying particular attention to the 'join', where it is important to ensure that the finished thickness is no more than the original.

Primer It is the priming paint which prevents the wood from becoming saturated with water. For that reason it must not only be applied well, but also before any stopping. Because the primer should penetrate into the wood, it must be put on by brush and

worked in well. A metallic wood primer with high water resistance is ideal. The first coat will be diluted with 20 per cent white spirit to allow for maximum penetration of the wood. Leave the first coat to dry overnight and then apply a second full-strength coat, leaving that overnight as well.

Assuming that all the major irregularities were filled at an earlier stage, those which now become apparent can be filled with a trowel cement. When the cement has hardened, rub it smooth with 220 grade wet and dry used dry, remove all the dust and add another coat of primer to the stopped areas. The cycle of stopping, rubbing down, priming should be repeated as many times as are necessary to achieve the required smoothness.

Most primers will cover at the rate of 60sq ft/pint (10sq m/litre). The correct thinner is white spirit. Apply the first (thinned) coat with a brush. Subsequent coats may be applied by brush, roller, pad or spray.

Undercoat Apply one coat of a general purpose undercoat. Next day, lightly rub it down with 320 grade wet and dry paper used wet, wash the surface thoroughly with clean water, then allow 2 or 3 hours for the water to evaporate completely before applying a second coat. On the following day, rub

down and wash as before, and if you are satisfied with the finish, move on to the final stage. Otherwise, try another undercoat.

Undercoat coverage is about 60sq ft/pint (10sq m/litre). Thinners will usually be white spirit. It may be applied by any means.

Top Coat This should be a synthetic resin-based general purpose enamel, and a coat should be applied about 24 hours after the last undercoat. Alternatively, a one-pot polyurethane enamel could be used. This type of paint has added methane oil to shorten the surface drying time from about 5 hours to 2 or 3. Extra weather protection can be achieved by applying a second coat of either. If this is done within 24 hours, no rubbing down will be necessary. If the interval is longer, to ensure good adhesion of the second coat, the first should be rubbed down with 400 grade waterproof paper used wet. Wash the surface thoroughly with clean water and allow 2 or 3 hours for it to dry before painting.

Enamel coverage is at the rate of about 60sq ft/pint (10sq m/litre). The correct thinner for either of these enamels is white spirit. Either may be applied by any means.

If the planks of a boat of carvel construction show no sign of working, a tougher and more waterproof paint specification may be used, as follows.

Above the Water Line: Ply and Cold Moulded

The burning off of paint from boats of laminate construction is not recommended. Rather than risk melting the glue and ruining the adhesion of the skins, it is better to use a chemical stripper. These constructions, having no planks to work against each other, can be painted with porous paints as described above or they might benefit from using a more waterproof and abrasion-resistant two-pot polyurethane.

An existing sound polyurethane finish can be freshened as follows. Start by rubbing down the whole surface with 180 grade waterproof paper used wet. Because these paints are very hard, it is possible that this will produce a polished effect. If this is so, it will be necessary to rub down again with 320 grade waterproof paper used dry. If there is

to be no change of colour, the enamel may now be applied, otherwise it will be necessary to apply the correct undercoat.

Primer As usual, bare wood must be primed

before any other paint or filler is applied. In preparation for two-pot polyurethane paints, there is a special clear primer or sealer which has to be used at full strength. However, these primers are for application to bare wood only, and if a patch of bare wood is to be painted, care must be taken to keep the primer off the existing paint. A second coat of primer should be applied between 6 and 24 hours after the first.

Coverage is at the rate of 70sq ft/pint (11sq m/litre). Thinner: International No 4. Can be applied by brush or spray.

Undercoat The first undercoat must be applied within 24 hours of the second primer or flaking might occur later. The base and hardener should be thoroughly mixed with a pallet knife in the recommended proportions, then allowed to stand for 10 minutes while the air bubbles disperse. The mixture has a usable life of 2 hours at 70°F (20°C), a period which decreases as the ambient temperature increases. This first undercoat should be allowed to harden for 6–24 hours before the final stopping with trowel cement or a two-part epoxy filler. After a further 24 hours smooth the whole surface with 220 grade waterproof paper used wet, wash it down thoroughly with clean water, wait 2–3 hours for all the water to evaporate, then apply a second undercoat. If more than 48 hours elapse between undercoats, it will be necessary to rub down with 320 grade paper used dry to provide a key for the next coat. The surface will have to be cleaned free of all dust before the next undercoat is applied. The cycle of stopping, rubbing down, undercoating, is repeated as often as is necessary to achieve the quality of finish required.

Coverage: 70sq ft/pint (11sq m/litre). Thinners: International No 2 (for spray thinning: No 10). Application: brush, roller, pad or spray.

Top Coat Having mixed the base and hardener as for the undercoat, two coats of the top coat are applied with an interval of 24 hours between.

Coverage: 70sq ft/pint (11sq m/litre). Thinners: International No 9 (for spray thinning: No 10). Application: brush, roller, pad or spray.

It will be a week or more, depending on the temperature, before the chemical reaction is complete and the surface is cured. During this time, it should be treated gently and protected from all liquids. Once it has cured, the surface can be polished using a car-type abrasive polish.

While painting with two-pot polyurethane paints, it is likely that the brush will have to be changed every half hour or so to avoid particles solidifying in the bristles.

Below the Water Line

Boats which are kept out of the water when not in use need no antifoul paint and the bottom is treated in the same way as the topside. In some ways, the choice of antifoul paint is one of the most difficult decisions which the boat owner has to make. The object of the exercise is to keep the bottom clean for the minimum cost. Antifoul paint is usually available in four or five strengths, the price being directly related. Examination of boats of similar construction which are used in a similar manner to yours will probably lead you to the cheapest antifoul paint which will keep your hull clean. Another factor which might affect your choice is the length of time the boat is likely to be out of the water between painting and launching. Soft antifoul paints should be immersed within 24 hours, whereas the hard versions can be left exposed to the air for up to ten weeks. Yet again, if you are after maximum performance, there are those with extra hard finishes which can be polished with waterproof paper used wet.

The poison in antifoul paint is dangerous. Never remove old paint by burning, dry scraping or any other dusty method unless full protective clothing is worn – and that should include an air-fed face mask. The alternative is to use a chemical stripper, but even then full protective clothing, including a face mask, should be worn.

Antifoul paint can be applied on top of old paint, but it is a process which is not necessarily straightforward. In addition to the two types of antifoul paint already

mentioned, there is a third. Conventional antifoul paints use a copper derivative as the poison, and this makes them unsuited for use on certain metal hulls. The potential electrolytic problem has been overcome by the development of a non-metallic poison – tri-butylin oxide. This is the basis of TBT and Tiger antifoul paints. Though developed specifically for metal hulls, they are frequently used on wooden hulls. So when considering applying antifoul paint on top of antifoul paint, all three, soft, hard and TBT, have to be considered. Sometimes the old coat will need sealing, sometimes it will not. The sealer will be either a metallic wood primer or perhaps a primer designed for underwater steel surfaces such as metallic primocon.

Hard or TBT antifoul paint can be applied directly to a hard antifouling, as can TBT be applied to TBT.

Hard or TBT antifoul paint can only be applied to a soft antifouling if that surface is first sealed with a metallic wood primer. The same primer must be used if a hard antifoul paint is to be applied to TBT.

Any antifoul paint to which a soft antifoul paint is to be applied (including the same type) should be sealed with a metallic steel primer. After 24 hours of applying any necessary sealing primer, the first coat of antifoul paint can be applied, perhaps followed by a second 24 hours later. The procedure for bare wood is as follows.

Primer The prepared wood should be dust free and wiped down with white spirit. The first coat should be a metallic wood primer thinned with 20 per cent white spirit, worked in well with a brush. A second, full-strength coat, should follow 24 hours later. When this second coat has hardened, probably the next day, trowel cement can be applied as necessary. After 16–24 hours this can be smoothed with 220 grade paper used dry, and then a further coat of primer added. Once again, the cycle of stopping, rubbing down, priming can be continued until the required quality of surface has been achieved. In any event, it is as well to apply at least four coats of primer because it is likely that, for some of the time at least, this will be the only protection on the wood.

Coverage: 70sq ft/pint (11sq m/litre). Thinner: white spirit. Application: first coat, brush; subsequent coats, brush, roller, pad or spray.

Antifoul Paint This will be applied directly to the primer with no further preparation. Ideally, a second coat will be applied after 24 hours, in which case no sealing will be necessary.

Coverage: 40–60sq ft/pint (7–10sq m/litre). Thinners: white spirit for soft, International No 2 for hard, No 3 for TBT.

Varnish

As with paint, there is a selection of types of varnish available. 'Common' varnish, which actually suits most purposes, can be obtained with a gloss or matt finish. There is also a one-pot polyurethane with the quicker drying time of three hours, and two-pot polyurethanes with the particularly hard finish available for use on oily wood, non-oily wood or with a matt finish.

Bare Wood It should be clean and free of grease, rubbed down with 280 grade dry paper, removing any sharp edges, then have the dust removed with a vacuum cleaner or by energetic brushing. Finally, wipe the whole surface down with white spirit.

Primer This may be either a clear wood primer or the chosen varnish diluted with 20 per cent of the appropriate thinner. Work it in well with a brush, paying particular attention to the end grain and, at 6–24 hour intervals, apply as many coats as are necessary until the grain will absorb no more.

Top Coat After 24 hours, apply the first full strength coat, followed at 24 hour intervals by four more. A finer finish can be achieved by rubbing down with 400 grade wet paper and wiping clean with thinners between coats. Generally, after suitable rubbing down, varnish can be applied over sound, old varnish, but in the case of two-pot polyurethanes, they can only be applied over similar varnish.

Conventional varnish: Coverage 80sq ft/pint (13sq m/litre). Thinner: white spirit. Application: primer by brush, other coats by brush or spray.

One-pot polyurethane and conventional matt: as above except for coverage which is 60sq ft/pint (10sq m/litre).

Two-pot polyurethane gloss and matt: Coverage: 70sq ft/pint (11sq m/litre). Thinner: International No 2. Application: primer by brush, others by brush or spray.

Two-pot polyurethane for oily wood: as above except for coverage which is 80sq ft/pint (13sq m/litre).

Application: GRP

Above the Water Line

It is assumed that the painting of GRP topsides will be for aesthetic reasons following the inevitable fading of the gel coat pigment with the passage of time. The paint used will be a two-pot polyurethane, itself a polyester, which is the only really suitable paint for application to GRP topsides.

Primer There is a special glass-fibre primer available which reacts chemically with the polyester of the gel coat forming a good bond and allowing for maximum adhesion of subsequent coats, provided they are applied within 6–24 hours. One coat is sufficient.

Coverage: 110sq ft/pint (18sq m/litre). Thinner: International No 7. Application: brush or spray.

Undercoat If the colour is not to be changed, omit this stage and go straight to 'top coat'. The base and hardener of the undercoat must be mixed thoroughly and allowed to stand for at least 10 minutes while the air bubbles disperse. Apply one coat. After 24 hours, rub down with 500 grade wet paper, then wipe the whole surface clean with thinners. Apply a second coat immediately, and after 24 hours, rub that down.

Coverage: 70sq ft/pint (11sq m/litre). Thinner: International No 2. Application: brush, roller or spray.

Top Coat Having mixed the two components thoroughly, as for earlier mixes, apply two coats with an interval of 24 hours between them, having rubbed down the first.

Coverage: 70sq ft/pint (11sq m/litre). Thinner: International No 9. Application: brush, roller or spray.

Below the Water Line

Primer This may be a similar primer to that used on the topsides or, as an alternative, it might be the Blake's Antifouling Primer.

Coverage: 80sq ft/pint (10sq m/litre). Thinner: Blake's No 3. Application: brush or roller.

Antifoul Paint Whichever primer has been used, the antifoul paint should be applied within 24 hours. Extra protection will be obtained if a second coat is applied 24 hours later.

Coverage: 50–55sq ft/pint (8–9sq m/litre). Thinners: Blake's No 3 or International No 3 for TBT and Micron 25, No 2 for hard racing types and white spirit for the others. Application: brush, roller or spray.

Osmosis

Protection If there is no evidence of osmosis, it might still be worth increasing the water resistance of the bottom of the boat. This can be effected by applying a two-pot polyurethane paint, as described earlier for the top sides.

Treatment If the hull has osmosis, all, or most of the gel coat will have been removed by grit blasting. It will take three months, or maybe more, before the hull is dry enough to proceed.

Primer One coat of an epoxy primer diluted with 15 per cent of thinner to allow it to penetrate the mat should be applied, and 24 hours later a second full strength coat should be added. Irregularities in the hull are then filled with a light-weight or low-density epoxy resin filler. This filler will have cured sufficiently for rubbing down after about eight hours, so it will probably be the next day before so doing. If the filler shows any sign of sweating, this should be washed off with fresh water and allowed to dry before applying another priming coat. Filling and priming can then be alternated until the hull is sufficiently smooth. The priming is finished with two more coats.

Coverage: 70sq ft/pint (8sq m/litre). Thinners: Blake's No 5 or International No 7. Application: brush, roller or spray.

The bottom is finished by the addition of an antifoul primer, if desired, followed by two coats of antifoul paint.

Application: Steel

Above the Water Line

Primer Apply by brush one coat of a general purpose primer, and after 24 hours add a second coat. Wait a further 24 hours and then fill any imperfections with a trowel cement, rub down and apply another priming coat. Carry on filling and priming at the appropriate intervals until the surface is smooth.

Coverage: 75sq ft/pint (12sq m/litre). Thinner: white spirit. Application: brush, roller or spray.

The undercoat and top coat will follow the same schedule as for the topsides of wood.

Below the Water Line

Primer Use a metal primer intended for use on steel such as International Metallic Primocon. Apply a second coat 1–21 days after the first and then apply a further three coats at 24 hour intervals.

Coverage: 75sq ft/pint (12sq m/litre). Thinner: white spirit. Application: brush, roller or spray.

Alternative Primer An alternative priming scheme is to use an etching primer for the first coat, following that with four or more coats of Blake's Chlorinated Rubber Anticorrosive, interspersed with trowel cement filling. An antifoul primer may also be added before the antifoul paint. If chlorinated rubber paints are used, they will never be removed with a chemical stripper – dry scraping or blasting must be used instead.

Antifoul Paint If the International primer was used, it will be necessary to wait a week before adding two coats of a hard antifoul paint, though one of the soft varieties could be added the next day.

If the Blake's chlorinated rubber and antifoul primers have been used, the antifoul paint can be added the next day. Once again, better protection will be obtained if two coats are applied.

Application: Aluminium

Above the Water Line

Primer The first priming coat should be with an etch primer if the bonding of subsequent coats is to be effective. When first applied, this primer is a pale yellow, becoming olive green or brown as it dries. If the colour does not change, it is either because the temperature was too low or because the metal was not clean enough. In either case, the answer is to remove it with a chemical stripper and, with more care, try again.

Coverage: 80sq ft/pint (13sq m/litre). Thinners: Blake's No 4 or International No 7. Application: brush, roller or spray.

The priming is finished with an alloy or metal primer, applying three coats and filling with trowel cement between them if necessary.

Coverage: 60sq ft/pint (10sq m/litre). Thinner: white spirit. Application: brush, roller or spray.

Undercoat and Top Coat This may be with either conventional synthetic resin-based paints or two-pot polyurethane. Use the same schedule as for the topsides of a wooden hull.

Below the Water Line

Primer The priming for the bottom is exactly the same as for the topsides except for the possible addition of one antifoul primer.

Antifoul Paint This must be one of the copper-free types such as TBT.

Application: Ferro-cement

Above the Water Line

Primer Apply one coat of a two-pack epoxy primer diluted with 15 per cent thinner. Follow that after 24 hours with another coat at full strength. A low-density or light-weight filler can now be used to improve the surface. Alternate filling and priming until the hull is sufficiently smooth and has at least four full-strength coats of primer.

Coverage: 50sq ft/pint (8sq m/litre). Thinners: Blake's No 5 or International No 7. Application: brush, roller or spray.

Undercoat and Top Coat The topsides can be finished with conventional paints, but two-pot polyurethanes are to be preferred. For details see Wood – Above the Water Line.

Below the Water Line

Primer The priming stages are exactly the same as for above the water line, the possible exception being the addition of an antifoul primer.

Antifoul Paint Ideally, two coats will be added.

Miscellaneous

Boot-Top Line

To avoid both the growth of weed near the water line and the appearance of floating above the marks which can be the result of simply raising the antifoul paint level, the best technique is to have a boot-top line. One of the hard antifoul paints should be used, and if it is of a colour which contrasts with both antifoul and topside paint, the effect can be quite pleasing.

Keels

Iron and Sheet Steel

Preparation These materials must be thoroughly cleaned with wire brush, scrapers, chipping hammer or emery cloth. If the corrosion is extensive or deeply pitted, it might be necessary to adopt the preparation suggested for steel hulls.

Primer Apply five coats of a metallic primer for steel and then leave for five days before antifouling.

Coverage: 75sq ft/pint (12sq m/litre). Thinner: white spirit. Application: brush, roller, pad or spray.

Lead

Preparation Lead should be thoroughly cleaned in a manner very similar to that employed with iron and steel, but perhaps with a little less vigour.

Primer Apply one coat of a two-pot self-etching primer, mixed according to the manufacturer's instructions and used within eight hours. This primer will both etch the surface to allow for good adhesion of the next coat and give protection. Never add a second coat.

Coverage: 80sq ft/pint (13sq m/litre). Thinner: for brush cleaning only, white spirit. Application: brush, roller, pad or spray.

Undercoat A two-pot epoxy resin coat is applied between 4 and 24 hours after the primer, and a further coat applied the next day.

Coverage: 50sq ft/pint (8sq m/litre). Thinners: Blake's No 5 or International No 7. Application: brush, roller, pad or spray.

Antifoul Paint The first coat should be applied 5–7 hours after the second coat of epoxy resin.

Galvanised Steel

Preparation Thoroughly clean and degrease the keel, using a proprietary agent if necessary, then proceed as for a lead keel, but with the addition of one more coat of epoxy resin paint. That will make three coats in total.

Antifoul Paint For all metal keels, ideally the antifoul paint should be one with no heavy metal content.

Decks

Wood

Laid decks are usually planked with teak or pitchpine and the best care for them is frequent and energetic scrubbing with salt water.

Plywood

These decks can be painted in the same way as topsides, except that some areas might be better treated with two coats of a non-slip deck paint instead of the undercoat and top coat.

Coverage: 70sq ft/pint (11sq m/litre). Thinner: white spirit. Application: brush, roller or pad.

An alternative way of making a non-slip paint is to add about a handful of silver sand to 1¾pt (1 litre) of the top coat and mix it thoroughly. Yet another alternative is to sprinkle the sand on to the top coat while it is still wet.

Canvas

Preparation If the paint on a canvas-covered deck is not kept intact there is a danger that it will become worn through and will have to be renewed. The problem with continued painting is that an accumulation of paint is difficult to remove, since neither burning nor chemical stripping is suitable. The only way is to remove loose paint carefully with a scraper and fill in the patches with new.

Primer Sufficient coats of metallic wood primer diluted with 20 per cent white spirit must be added to completely impregnate the canvas and make a continuous surface.

Undercoat One coat is sufficient.

Top Coat This can be one or two coats of proprietary deck paint, or the paint of your choice with sand added, as above.

Bilges

Preparation The almost inevitable accumulation of oily and greasy water in the bilge must be completely removed. This will usually mean the use of a degreasing agent and copious quantities of water. After the sludge has been removed, wash the whole area thoroughly with fresh water.

Painting When the bilge has dried, apply two coats of an appropriate primer, followed by two coats of a special bilge paint.

If the bilge has already been painted, it will still need degreasing and a wash with fresh water, after which the bare patches can be primed before application of the bilge paint.

Steel Tanks

Preparation Those tanks made of steel are the only ones which will need painting. The inside will be best cleaned by shot blasting and if the equipment is available that would be the best way of preparing the exterior. The alternative is a wire brush or a disc grinder, perhaps.

Painting The exterior will be well protected by two coats of primer and two of bilge paint. If possible, four coats of epoxy primer should be applied to the interior. If access to the interior of the tank is not possible, the rusting problem can be delayed by keeping the tank as full as possible.

Condensation

Sometimes condensation in a boat is impossible to avoid. It is not always convenient to have a flow of air throughout the boat, particularly when making to windward. However, there are such things as anti-condensation paints which set up a high heat insulating barrier and so minimise the problem.

Painting Apply an appropriate priming paint, followed by an undercoat which will probably be white. After 24 hours apply one coat of the anti-condensation paint. Alternatively, the anti-condensation paint can be applied directly to existing paintwork if it is sound and rubbed down. If the colour of the anti-condensation paint is not acceptable, cover it with a half-and-half mixture of undercoat and top coat of the preferred colour. Applying enamel alone will impair the insulating efficiency of the anti-condensation paint.

Buoyancy Compartments

Most sailing dinghies are built with some sealed buoyancy which is completely inaccessible once the boat has been completed. If access to such a compartment becomes available while repairing a wooden dinghy, it will be well worth the effort of applying several coats of a metallic primer.

Spars

Wood

Most spars are made of spruce, a light straight-grained wood. Unfortunately, it is also quite soft and vulnerable to tapping halyards and other apparently harmless abrasions. A good sound coat of paint or varnish will go a long way towards protecting the wood. In addition, those hollow spars made of two or four pieces have glues which might need protecting from the weather. Varnish can be applied in very much the same way as it is to any other wood. However, there might come a time when that is no longer acceptable, for one reason or another. Badly discoloured wood can be disguised with paint, probably one light in colour to reduce expansion owing to heat. If painting does become necessary, remove all traces of the varnish first, because paint will not adhere to it properly.

Alloy

Most alloy spars are anodised and paint simply will not stick to anodising. However, those which are not anodised, or those from which the anodising has been removed, can be painted. A conventional paint could be used, but a two-pot polyurethane is to be preferred. First, give the spar a good rub down with 320 grade wet paper, then apply one coat of a self-etching primer, followed by two coats of a primer for metal. Finish off with two or three coats of a two-pot polyurethane paint.

7 Rigging

Getting up the Mast

The ability to get to the extremities of a boat is a desirable requirement for all skippers. A bosun's chair should be an obligatory piece of equipment on all boats with masts. The modern canvas version, complete with pockets for tools, has a lot in its favour when compared with a plank of wood and a bucket. But when it comes to standing up to work on the truck, a nice solid base causes all the disadvantages to pale to insignificance.

Bosun's Chair

When making a chair, take the trouble to make it properly. It might not look much, but your life will depend on it. You will need a piece of wood about 18in (450mm) long, 5in (125mm) wide and 1in (25mm) thick. Drill a hole near each corner through which the rope strop will pass, then fair off the corners and chamfer the edges. The strop is made from one length of rope, the ends of which are joined with a short splice beneath

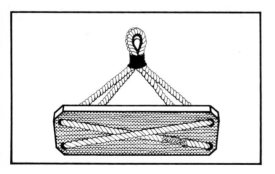

the seat. The two leads of the strop should diagonally cross the seat in order that some support remains if the wood breaks. Seize a thimble into the bights of both strops and the job is finished. The length of the strops should be such that there is only just enough

room to get in and out. The longer they are, the more likely it is that you will have to stand to get near the mast head.

It is usually safer if a man up the mast is tended by a competent seaman on deck, but occasionally it might be necessary for the man in the chair to control his own descent. If this is the case, send him up on a fibre-rope halyard and get him to tie the following knot. He should grasp both parts of the halyard with his right hand, sufficiently tightly to support his weight when the halyard has been cast off the winch, which should be so done as soon as he is ready. With the slack now available, he can now pull a bight of the halyard through the strop of the chair with his left hand, and by squeezing that with the halyard just above the chair can transfer the support of his weight to the left hand. The final move is to pull up enough slack on the tail of the halyard to pass a bight over the head and round the whole body and chair and work it up snugly to a cow hitch just below the thimble. By feeding the tail of the halyard into the hitch, a controlled descent can be made. For the first attempt at tying this knot it is worth going just a little way up the mast.

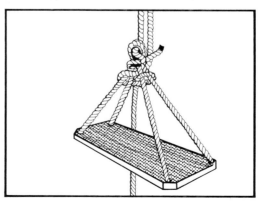

Rigging

The inspection, removal and replacing of rigging will mostly be performed from the bosun's chair, and it is while so doing that the opportunity should be taken to look out for wear and chafe, whether it be on the rigging or the sails. The result might be a length of polythene pipe put on a new length of rigging before the final terminal is fitted, but remember also that baggy wrinkle has its place as well.

Baggy Wrinkle One of the oldest, not to say impressive, anti-chafe device is made remarkably quickly. Cut lengths of old rope into equal lengths and separate the strands. Take two lengths of line and put a figure-of-eight knot in the pair, about 6in (150mm) from an end. Stretch the lines taut. Put the bight of one of the strands over the lines and bring the ends up between the lines. Haul it tight up to the figure-of-eight knot. Add a second strand and haul that up tight against the first. Keep adding strands until you have

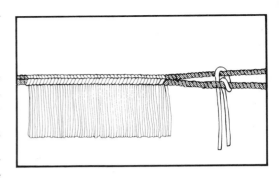

the right length. Hold all the strands in position with a reef knot in the parallel lines. Tease out the fibres of the strands and you have a length of baggy wrinkle.

When attaching the baggy wrinkle to a shroud or stay, tie the lower end first and wind the baggy wrinkle round and up, finally tying the upper end.

Rope

Materials

In rigging, there are two types of rope, fibre and wire. Fibre ropes may be made of natural materials like jute or hemp, but nowadays it is more likely that those encountered will be of man-made fibres such as nylon, polyester and polypropylene. Wire ropes are of either galvanised steel or stainless steel.

Construction

Whether of fibre or wire, the basic material is formed into relatively thin fibres or wires which are twisted together to form strands. A number of these strands are twisted together, or laid up, to form a laid rope. Alternatively, fibre strands may be woven or plaited together to form plaited rope. By varying the number of wires or fibres in the strands, the number of strands and the way in which they are formed, a diversity of characteristics can be imparted to the rope. Strength, elasticity and flexibility are those most commonly varied to suit differing requirements. Brief descriptions of the commonly found constructions follow.

Fibre

Hawser laid The most common, sometimes the only laid rope seen on board modern boats. Three strands are laid up around each other in a clockwise direction. It is said to be of a right-handed lay.

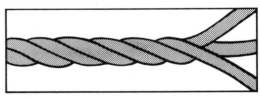

16 plait Sixteen strands plaited, sometimes around a three-strand core.

8-plait Eight strands which may be plaited around a three-strand core or one of straight multifilaments.

Braidline Plaited sheath around plaited core.

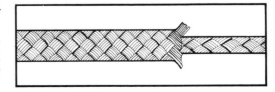

Multiplait Eight strands, two pairs of which are laid up in a clockwise direction, the other two pairs being laid up in an anti-clockwise direction.

Wire

6 × 7 Six strands, each of seven wires, laid up around a core which might be of fibre or another strand of seven steel wires.

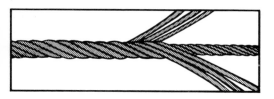

6 × 19 Six strands, each of nineteen wires, laid up around a fibre core.

1 × 19 One strand of nineteen wires. This is usually only made with stainless steel wire and used for standing rigging.

Faults

All the faults associated with rope, whether it is of fibre or wire are caused by either chafe or corrosion.

Chafe This is caused by friction and so is always associated with moving rope – the running rigging. A common cause is the use of blocks with inadequate sized sheaves. The diameter of sheave should be four or five times that of fibre rope or twelve times that of wire. The radius of the groove in the sheave should be a little larger than that of the rope.

Winches, fairleads, bitts and cleats should be examined regularly to ensure that they are not unnecessarily abrading rope. If ropes are to remain in a fairlead for any length of time, the length likely to be chafed can be protected by parcelling or a length of hose.

Fibre ropes can be chafed from the inside if grit or sand or even salt particles are present. It is good practice to keep them clean by washing in clean, fresh water. Never use detergent on natural fibre ropes.

Corrosion Man-made fibre ropes are virtually immune to natural corrosion, but can still be ruined if brought into contact with some chemicals or heat. It is good practice to stow them well away from lead-acid batteries, paint and its associated liquids and exhaust pipes.

Galvanised wire rope will rust in time, usually as a result of the galvanising wearing away. This is almost unavoidable if the piece of rigging is a halyard or a stay up which is run a hanked sail. The life of the wire can be extended by cleaning and protecting it regularly. This involves giving it a thorough cleaning with a wire brush and then applying a liberal coating of boiled linseed oil. The oil will solidify to form a protective skin which will keep the weather out, for a short time at least. Boiled oil dries most readily in good paint drying conditions. Another task worth undertaking occasionally is the removal of the servings which should be on all the hand splices. This can become a water trap, particularly at the lower ends.

Stainless wire rope, in theory at least, is corrosion resistant. Its life is normally terminated when it 'strands' or when it becomes brittle. The first is caused by abuse. The second often occurs at the entry to terminal fittings where continuous slight movement work hardens the wire and it becomes brittle. There is no visual warning of this happening, but it could take seven or eight years to manifest itself. If the terminal fitting can be removed (and replaced), an occasional inspection and bending of a strand should alleviate any doubts.

Tools

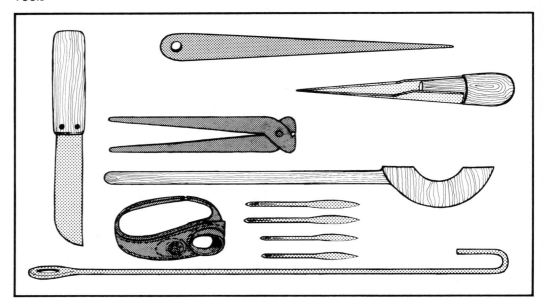

It is possible to improvise some of the rigger's tools but, as in most spheres, the job will be that much easier if the correct ones are available. A knife, sail-maker's palm, needles, fid, spike, splicing needle, serving mallet and wire nippers would make a good complete kit, but individual repairs will require only a selection, of course.

Repairs

The work required on rope, whether fibre or wire, halyard or warp, is nearly always concerned with just its ends. These may be finished with a simple whipping or an eye, or they may be joined to other ropes. These joins may be fibre to fibre, fibre to wire or even fibre to chain. There follow examples of the techniques employed to achieve those ends with modern materials.

Whipping

There is no demand, other than as a temporary measure while engaged in splicing, to whip the ends of wire rope, but there are many ways of doing so to the ends of fibre ropes. The three described will cover all eventualities. The first is not very secure but there are circumstances when neither of the other two can be applied. Whenever possible, one of the two more secure whippings should be used.

Common Whipping Lay a length of whipping twine along the rope as illustrated, and with the working end take tight turns round both rope and that end of the twine, towards the end of the rope. When nearly enough turns have been taken, double back the first

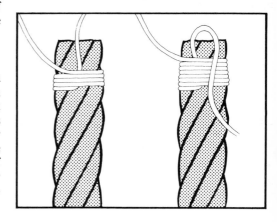

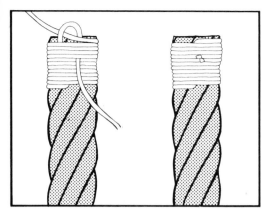

end, leaving a loop beyond the end of the rope. Finish taking the turns and then pass the working end through the loop. Pull on the short end to trap the working end, which is then cut off short prior to being pulled under the turns by the short end. Finally, cut off the surplus short end.

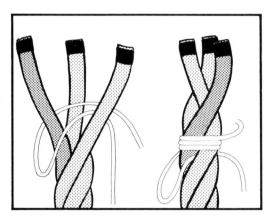 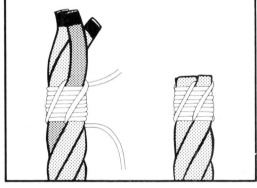

Sail-maker's Whipping This can only be applied to three-strand rope. Seal the ends of each strand with heat or tape and unlay the rope for a distance equal to three times its diameter. Hold it in the left hand with the strands pointing up. Pass a bight of whipping twine between the two strands facing you and over the distant middle one. Adjust the twine so that the short end is 6in (150mm) long and the bight is a similar length. Hold the bight, the short end of the whipping twine and the rope in the left hand.

With the long end of the twine take tight turns around the rope, working against the lay (that is, clockwise when viewed from

above) until the length of the whipping is the same as the diameter of the rope.

Release the bight from the left hand and take it up and over the end of the same strand around which it was originally passed, taking care to ensure that it follows the lay of the rope exactly, with no twists.

Pull on the short end to tighten this bight, then lead the short end up the lay of the rope and reef knot it to the other end in the middle of the rope and out of sight.

Cut off the surplus rope. If it is synthetic this can be done with a heated knife blade, so sealing the end and making for an even neater finish.

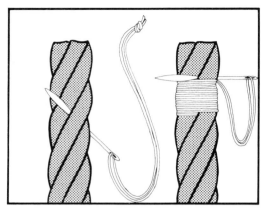
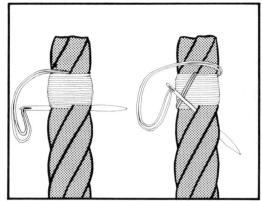

Palm and Needle This is described as for application to a three-strand rope, but the principle can be equally well applied to plaited ropes. It looks very similar to a sail-maker's whipping. With practice, it can be worked with the twine doubled, which is both quicker and aesthetically more pleasing.

Thread the needle and knot the end of the twine. Hold the rope in the left hand. Pass the needle through the middle of one strand, through the rope and out between the other two strands. Pull the twine reasonably tight and bury its knot in the fibres of the strand. Taking tight turns against the lay, make the whipping as long as the diameter of the rope.

At the top, pass the needle through one strand, entering and leaving apparently between strands.

Follow the lay down the whipping and pass the needle through the next strand, again apparently entering and leaving between strands.

Follow the lay up the whipping and finish by passing the needle between two strands and out through the third.

The end of the whipping twine can be made more secure by passing it backwards and forwards a couple of times through the strand. Trim the end as before.

Eyes

Formed just in the rope, it will be known as a soft eye. When formed around a thimble, which will minimise chafe of the rope, it will be known as a hard eye. Soft eyes are more usual in the ends of mooring lines, when they will be relatively large. Hard eyes are more usual in the ends of sheets or wire rigging.

Three-Strand (Fibre Rope)

Heat seal or tape the ends of the individual strands. Make a short (three or four turn) palm-and-needle whipping fifteen rope diameters from the end and unlay the strands to it. Holding the rope in the left hand, form an eye of the desired size, with one strand above, one below and one lying along the rope. It is important to achieve this position with no twisting of the rope, otherwise the finished eye will be twisted.

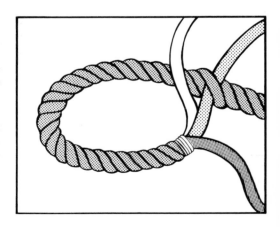

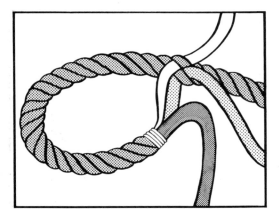

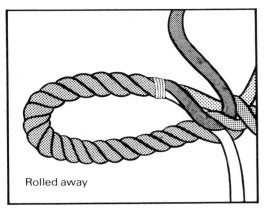

Rolled away

Again with the aid of the fid, tuck each strand once more, ensuring that each tucking strand alternates over and under strands of the parent rope. Work up these second tucks until it is all snug, then put in a third series. The splice can be tapered by passing a fourth tuck with half the fibres from each strand.

Pass the fid up through the strand facing you and follow it with the centre of the 'tucking' strands which was lying along the rope. Remove the fid and push it through the top strand, following with the upper 'tucking' strand. Roll the top of the part splice away from you until the unused strand is on top. Push the fid through this third strand and follow it with the third 'tucking' strand. Remove the fid. Work up all the strands until it all looks tight, neat and tidy.

Finish the splice by trimming the six ends with a hot knife to melt the ends into the lay oɪ the rope.

Serving

The three-strand eye splice, and all other splices, can be finished by serving them with marlin or other line. Secure the eye to your right and stretch the rope out to your left, preferably by using a purchase or winch. Experience will tell you how long the serving line should be. If that sounds like a long-winded way of suggesting you guess at its length, that is because it is. With the right thumb, hold a short end of the serving line in the lay about six diameters from the eye. Take tight turns around the rope and this short end, working against the lay. After a couple of turns, the end should be effectively jammed.

Put the turns on as tightly as possible, right up to the eye. With the end of the serving line held against the eye with the little finger of the right hand, loosen the last six turns enough to allow this end to be passed back underneath them, then do just that. Retighten these last six turns, trapping the end of the serving line as tightly as possible. Pull through all the surplus line and put a hitch in the end to enable more tension to be put on it with a spike. When it is as tight as you can possibly make it, trim off the end neatly.

A serving board or mallet should be used to put the serving on tightly, particularly for larger and wire ropes. The final tightening can be effected by making the marlin-spike hitch around a hammer head and using the weight of that to jerk the turns up tight.

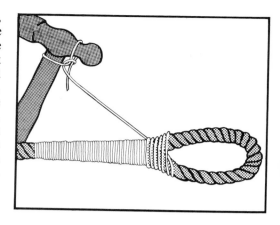

Multiplait – Sew and Serve

Allow a tail of eight times the diameter of the eye required. Taper the end third of the tail by cutting out strands at intervals. Sew the untapered part of the tail to the parent rope, putting a row of stitches down from the eye on one side and back up to the eye on the other. Marl the tapered part of the tail prior to serving the whole.

A small variation allows for the making of an eye in the middle of a rope, perhaps for use as jib sheets. Form the eye around a thimble, then sew the two parts together. Serve up to the eye.

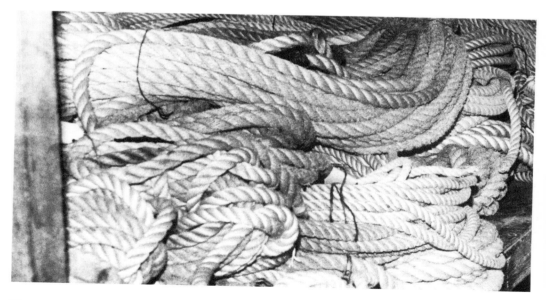

16 plait

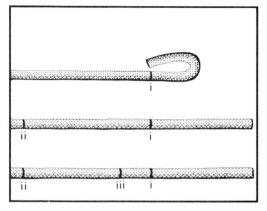

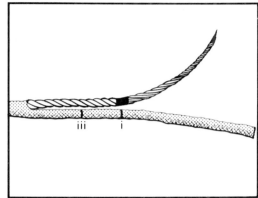

Using the thimble as a guide if it is to be a hard eye, mark point (i) to indicate the size of the eye required. Mark a second point (ii) 12in (300mm) along from (i). The length of rope required for the eye is the distance from (i) to the end. Measure that distance from (ii) towards (i) and mark it as point (iii).

Using a spike gently, open up the sheath until the core can be prised out, then work it out completely. Put tape around the core at a position equivalent to point (iii), then taper it from there to the end.

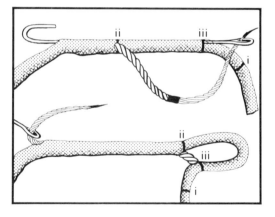

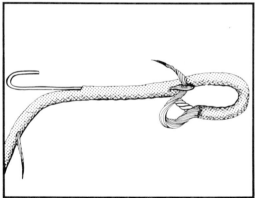

At a position 10in (250mm) further along than point (ii), insert the splicing needle through the sheath and work it along, between core and sheath until it comes out at point (iii). Pass the tapered end of the core through the eye of the needle, then withdraw the needle carefully, easing the core into the sheath, along the inside and out again with the needle.

Unpick and taper the end of the sheath. Insert the needle through the sheath again, this time about 5in (125mm) from the position where the core re-enters it, and out at that point. Thread the end of the sheath through the eye of the needle and so pull that right through.

Work up the eye until it looks neat and tidy by pulling on the ends of both core and sheath, then cut off the surplus. Roll the splice between the palms of the hands or roll it underfoot and the ends will disappear.

8 Plait (Dinghies Only)

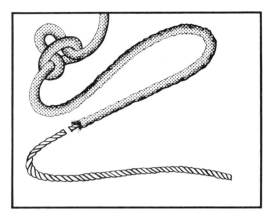

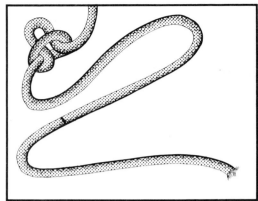

Because a length of the core is removed, this splice weakens the rope considerably, but is strong enough for use on a dinghy.

Make a marlin spike hitch 6ft (2m) from the end. If the end has been heat sealed, cut it off and work the sheath back until 30in (700mm) of the core has been bared, then cut it off.

Work the sheath back to its original position, such that the end 30in (700mm) is 'core-less'.

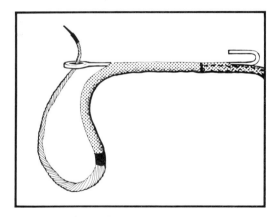

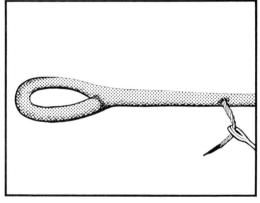

Insert the splicing needle through the sheath ½in (12mm) before the start of the core and work it out 11in (275mm) towards the end. Taper the end of the sheath and thread it through the eye of the needle.

Withdraw the needle completely, and with it the sheath which is now replacing the core. Work it all up tight and neat and apply a moderate load to the eye before cutting off the surplus.

A thimble can be inserted, but small adjustments must be made to the measurements.

6 × 7 Galvanised Wire

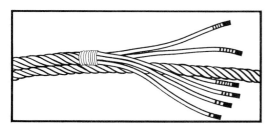

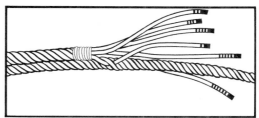

Put a short serving on the wire a distance from the end of thirty-five times its diameter. Whip or tape the end of each of the six strands, unlay them to the serving and cut out the heart.

Form the size of eye required by seizing the two parts together. Tension and support the wire at a good working height and give yourself enough room to get to both sides. Place three strands on either side of the standing part of the wire.

Using a flat spike (screwdriver?) to raise it, tuck the first strand under the most convenient strand in the standing part, against the lay. It is often easier to insert the spike a short distance from the final location of the strand, take the tuck alongside it and then wind the spike along the wire, opening up the lay as it goes and work the strand along with it.

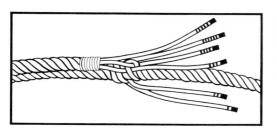

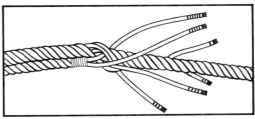

Tuck the next three strands successively in a very similar manner, working in the same direction so that all the tucks are against the lay.

For the moment, miss out the fifth strand and tuck the sixth under two strands.

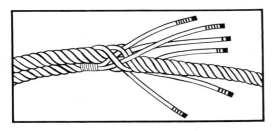

Now go back to the fifth and tuck that under one strand and out between the two under which the sixth passes. Work all the strands up tightly and neatly and check that there is just one appearing from between each pair of strands of the standing part.

Put in a second series of tucks, using each strand in turn this time and ensuring that each follows the over-one, under-one pattern. Then put in a third series.

Take out a third of the wires in each strand, lashing them out of the way, probably to the eye, and then take a series of tucks with the remaining two-thirds. When that is neat and tidy, remove another third of the wires and make the final series of tucks with the remaining third.

Nip off all the protruding wire. Grease the splice well and parcel it with a 1in (25mm) wide bandage of sail cloth, working with the lay, towards the eye.

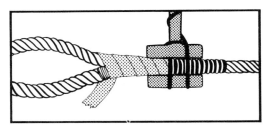 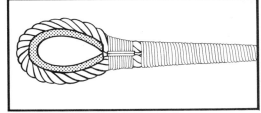

Finally, serve the splice against the lay. If the parcelling and serving are applied in the same direction, the parcelling will bunch up.

If a hard eye is required, it will take four or five seizings around it to hold the wire well into the eye during the splicing.

An alternative to the conventional hard eye is that known as the hawser eye. This is a soft eye into which a thimble is seized when the splice has been completed.

Stainless Wire Eye

Stainless wire can be hand spliced in the same way as galvanised wire, but because it is much springier, it is that much more difficult. There are a number of terminal eye fittings available for both types of wire, but most require pressing or compressing equipment. The Norseman terminal, a description of the fitting of which follows, is particularly useful for fitting to stainless wire and has no need of special tools.

Tape the end and cut or saw through it to leave a clean finish. Place the terminal body over the end of the wire and then lock it in a vice.

Prise away the outer strands of wire to expose the inner strand. Fit the core over this centre strand and push it on so far that the amount of strand protruding is equal to the diameter of the wire.

Pull the wire and core down into the body, bending the outer wires back over the core, using a wrench, if necessary.

Gently screw on the end fitting for most of

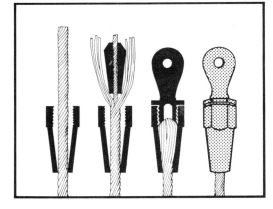

its travel and then remove it to ensure that the outer wires are lying symmetrically over the cone. If they are not, rearrange them.

When all is correct, fit the locking nut to the end fitting, fill it with silicon rubber sealant, add a thread locking sealant and screw it home, using a tommy bar. Finally, tighten the locking nut.

Joins

Three-strand Short Splice

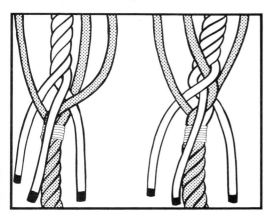

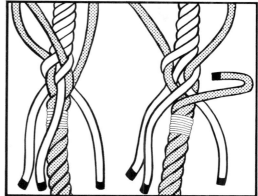

Put a constrictor knot on each rope, fifteen times its diameter from the end. This knot will act as a temporary whipping. Heat seal or tape each strand and unlay it to the whipping. Marry the ropes together so that any one strand of one rope is lying between two of the other. Lead the strands of one rope along the length of the other and lash them in that position.

Tuck the free strands over and under, against the lay, until three full tucks have been put in. This splice can be tapered, but it is one which is basically unsightly because of its bulk, and there is little that can be done to change that.

In a similar manner, put in three tucks with the other three strands. Cut off the whippings and remove the surplus strands with a hot blade, melting them into the lay.

Three-strand Long Splice

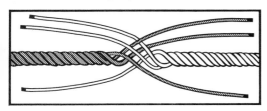

Put constrictor knots on each rope at a distance of thirty-five diameters from the end. Unlay all six strands and marry them up as for a short splice.

Remove the whipping from one rope and

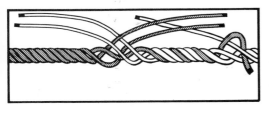

start unlaying one strand, laying in one from the second rope as you do so. Near the end of the strand, join them with an overhand knot.

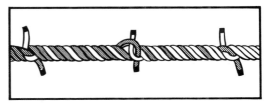

Remove the whipping from the second rope and unlay one of its strands while laying in one from the other rope, again finishing with an overhand knot.

The third pair of strands are simply joined with an overhand knot.

Finish off the splice by putting a serving over each knot or over the whole splice.

Rigging

Three-Strand to Wire

This splice is made in exactly the same way as a short three-strand splice, with two exceptions. The first is that the heart of the wire must be removed. The second is that the six wires are paired off, both when tucking

and being tucked under.

The splice can be neatened by tapering and will look and handle better if parcelled and served.

Plaited (Three-strand Core) to Wire

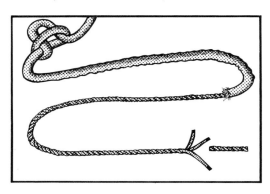

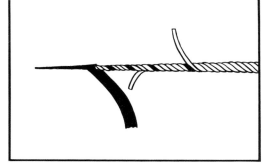

Put a marlin-spike hitch in the rope 6ft (2m) from its end. Work the sheath back to expose 3ft (1m) of the core. Cut 6in (150mm) off the core and tape or heat seal its three strands.

Taper the wire over a length of 8in (200mm) and put tape over the taper.

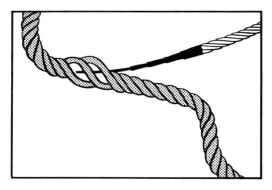

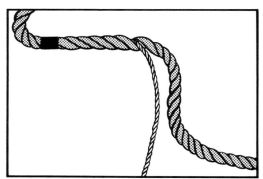

About 30in (750mm) from the end of the core, open up the lay enough to get the end of the wire in and tape it there.

Hold the end of the wire and the core in the left hand and wind the core around the wire with the right, opening up the lay enough to allow the wire to find its way to the centre.

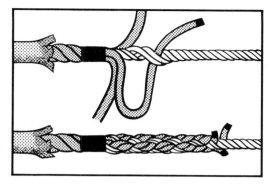

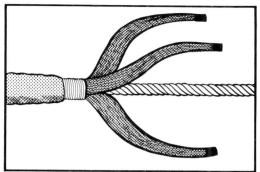

Tape or whip the core to the wire 8in (200mm) from the end and unlay the strands to this point.

Tuck the strands of the core under pairs of the wire strands, against the lay. Complete three full tucks, followed by two tapered. Remove two pieces of tape or whipping.

Slide the sheath out to its natural extension, which should be overlapping the inner core by some 8in (200mm) or so. Put a whipping on the sheath and wire close to the inner splice.

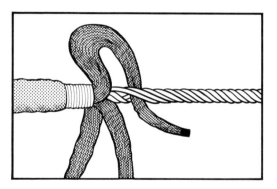

Unlay the sheath to the whipping, divide the strands into three equal bunches and tape the ends.

Tuck these three strands under pairs of wires, but this time go with the lay. This means that each strand is successively tucked under, or spiralled around the same strands of wire. If the sequence is followed meticulously, the effect will be to hide the wire completely for the length of the splice. The end product is of a particularly neat appearance if each of the five required tucks is progressively tapered.

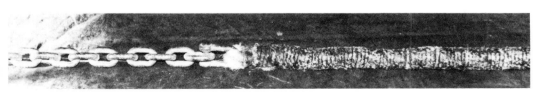

Plaited (with Plaited Core) to Wire

This splice can be formed in a very similar manner. The only differences are that the tapered wire has to be worked gently down the centre of the core, rather than being 'wound' into it, and this core has to be stranded and made up into three strands before splicing it into the wire. The sheath is dealt with in exactly the same way as above.

Three-strand to Chain

This splice is started in the same way as for an eye splice, except that one strand is unlaid for an extra 6in (150mm).

The two odd strands are passed through the end link of chain. The long strand is then unlaid further while one of the short ones is laid up in its place.

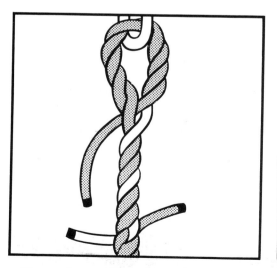

The ends are joined with an overhead knot.

The third strand is tucked as for a short splice, with the fourth and fifth tucks being tapered.

The whole splice should be served.

The maximum strength of this splice is two-thirds the strength of the rope, so probably it is not suitable for attaching a warp to an anchor. It is intended to be used for splicing a tail to chain which is required to pass through a block.

Bottle Screws

Turnbuckles, rigging or bottle screws are available made of galvanised steel, stainless steel and bronze. They are used to tension rigging and guard-rails. The principle of operation is based on two opposite-handed female threads at either end of a body, into which are screwed fittings for attachment to rigging, chainplates, or whatever. As the body is turned, both screws either screw in or screw out. The overall length increases or decreases.

Faults

The only faults which occur with bottle screws are seizing up, threads wearing and stripping and the ends getting bent. The first usually only applies to those of galvanised steel and the other two can only be safely rectified by replacement.

Cleaning

It might take a vice, freeing oil and a lot of effort, but bottle screws can be dismantled. It is usually the lower end which is most corroded, because the water can lie on the head of the thread. The cleaning process has almost been completed by the act of dismantling, but the last signs of corrosion, salt, verdigris or other foreign bodies can be removed with a wire brush. When it is thoroughly clean, reassemble it with a light smear of grease on the threads and ensure that both run freely.

Fitting

When the bottle screw is replaced, ensure that the upper screw is threaded left handed. Under tension rope tends to unlay. This means that conventional, or right-handed rope, will do so in such a way as to screw in a left-hand thread, a preferable circumstance to the alternative.

Whether securing bottle screws or shackles, soft galvanised wire is the easiest to use. As illustrated, two turns in a figure-of-eight pattern is sufficient. Cut off the surplus and tuck the remaining end well away.

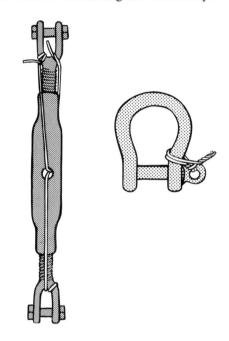

Protection

As they are prone to corrosion, steel bottle screws need protecting. After setting up the rigging or guard-rails, the visible threads should be cleaned of grease and a good coating of lanolin applied. This is not a lubricant, but it is more resistant than grease to the onslaught of water and offers better protection. Fill all the cavities to exclude the water and pay particular attention to the lower end of those mounted vertically. Parcel the exposed threads with canvas insulating tape and then varnish that. Finally, lock off the bottle screw with lock nuts, split pins or by wiring.

Blocks

Modern tufnol blocks need nothing more than an occasional face lift in the form of a wipe over with an oily rag. Wooden blocks with steel pins need greasing regularly and pins renewed occasionally, both of which necessitate dismantling the block.

Dismantling

If the screws and retaining pads are removed from each cheek, it is a relatively simple task to drive out the pin and catch the sheave. Use a drift which is smaller than the pin or you might end up with a split cheek.

Winches

Provided they are kept lubricated, modern winches should give many years of trouble-free service. The only parts likely to fail are the pawls and springs. The drum should be cleaned regularly to avoid unnecessary wear on the ropes.

Cleaning

Wash all winches with fresh water after every sail and then dry them with a chamois leather. Dirt deposits can be removed from chromed and stainless winches by gentle use of a non-abrasive liquid cleaner, but no sort of cleaner should ever be used on anodised aluminium.

Lubrication

Each month, all winches should be lightly oiled and greased. When laying up, fitting out and, two or three times during the season, they should be dismantled, thoroughly cleaned and lubricated.

What follows is a description of the dis-

mantling and lubrication of a fairly typical winch, the two-speed Lewmar No 16. Before dismantling a particular winch, it would be as well to have the manufacturer's service manual available.

1 Remove the top circlip with a small screwdriver or knife blade.

2 Lift off the drum.

3 Wash the centre stem, roller bearings and drum bore with paraffin. Dry them with a non-fluffy cloth.

4 Lightly oil the top pawls.

5 Remove the centre spindle key and slide out the spindle.

6 Clean the spindle, grease it lightly and oil the pawls.

7 Remove the gear, clean and lightly grease it.

Reassemble the winch in the reverse order and check it for correct operation. To avoid undue delays while cruising or frustration when dismantling winches away from the immediate services of a good chandler, carry

8 Reassemble the spindle and the gears. Oil the pawls in the winch base.

a selection of the parts which might need replacing as a result of damage or loss. These would include pawls and springs, circlips and washers. Most manufacturers will supply a spares kit with such items.

8 Sails

Construction

Today, cotton sails are as rare as they were once prolific. Those made of polyester, more usually referred to by the trade names of Terylene and Dacron, fulfil such a high percentage of current demand that they will be the only ones considered here.

Panels of polyester sail cloth are woven in a manner very similar to that used in any other type of weaving. Length-wise threads of polyester (the warp) are interwoven with similar threads (the weft) from right to left and back again.

When cut to the required shape, the panels are sewn together at the 'seams' with either two or three rows of stitching, depending on the weight and size of the sail.

The edges of the sail are folded over and sewn in a hem, known in nautical circles as 'tabling'.

The luff, and for a mainsail the foot, and in addition if it is a gaff mainsail the head, will usually have a fibre or wire 'bolt' rope sewn in the tabling.

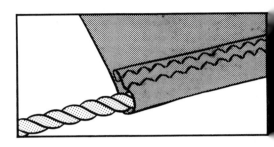

Each corner of the sail needs an eye which is used to secure the sail when it is in use. In the case of a triangular head sail they might be hard eyes spliced in the ends of the luff bolt rope. Others may be eyes punched or sewn into the sail or cringles which are spliced in.

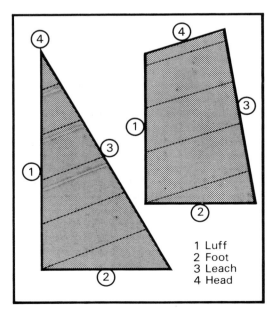

1 Luff
2 Foot
3 Leach
4 Head

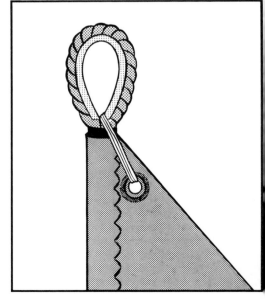

Faults

Apart from accidental damage which normally results in a tear, the most common problems encountered are staining and chafe. With care and forethought both can be minimised, but it is almost inevitable that eventually both will have to be dealt with.

Too much grease and oil on the rigging or snap shackles is a frequent source of stains on sails and the way to avoid it is more than obvious. Rust stains can only be prevented by keeping the sail well away from sources of rust. Unfortunately, that is not always as easy as it might sound – even with the use of 'stainless' rigging. The stowing of wet sails in cotton bags will lead, sooner or later, to mildew stains transferring themselves from bag to sail; always use polyester bags, therefore.

A common point of chafe is on the foot of a headsail where it comes into contact with the pulpit or guard-rail. A higher cut sail is a safer remedy than lowering the pulpit. Another point is where the leech of the mainsail fouls the backstay or other part of the rigging. Cringles which have distorted under load can lead to chafe of the cloth. Sails can also be chafed by particles of salt trapped in the weave, so after a salt-water soaking they should be washed, or at least rinsed thoroughly in fresh water.

Polyester deteriorates in the ultra-violet part of sunlight. A sail cover will protect that part of the sail normally exposed when it is stowed on the boom.

To avoid 'cracking', prior to being bagged, a sail should be folded loosely in zigzags down the luff, then rolled, once again loosely, from luff to clew. The bag should be large enough to take the sail without compressing it.

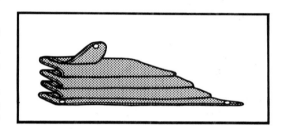

Cleaning

Most sails should be washed at least once each year and it is likely that some stains will be first noticed and dealt with then. But, generally speaking, most stains will be removed more easily if attacked soon after they occur.

Washing

Small sails can be washed by hand in a bath, using hot water and detergent. Others should be laid flat, if necessary section by section, and scrubbed with a stiff brush, again using hand-hot water and detergent. When laying the sail out, make sure that the surface is smooth and has no chafe points. In either case, rinse the sail well in clean water. No harm will result if the sail, or part of it, is left to soak overnight to remove stubborn grime.

Blood Soaking in a biological soap powder is one way of removing blood stains. If that is not effective, try a weak solution of oxalic acid. In stages, work up to a maximum strength of one part acid to twenty parts of water. It is a poison, so wash your hands well after using it and rinse the sail well in fresh water.

Mildew Brush off as much of the mildew as possible and then soak the stained area in a solution of one part of domestic bleach to ten parts of water. This should not be used if the sail is made of nylon.

Oil and grease A domestic cleaner based on carbon tetrachloride will probably work, but if it does not, brush a solvent and detergent mixture such as Polyclens well into the material. When it has pickled for about fifteen minutes wash it thoroughly in clean water. Yet another possibility is to use a hand cleaner such as Swarfega.

Paint and Varnish If tackled early enough, white spirit, or another appropriate thinner, will do the job. Whatever is used, avoid alkaline paint strippers.

Rust A very weak solution of oxalic acid might remove rust stains, but if not, try a slightly stronger solution. Limit the strength to one part acid to twenty parts water. If that is ineffective, try soaking the sail in a solution of one part of hydrochloric acid to fifty parts of water. After either of the above, rinse the sail well in clean water.

Tar Dab the tar with white spirit, or if that fails, solvent naphtha.

Repairs

Tools

A full sail repair kit comprises: fid, knife, needles, twine, wax, palm, hook, pricker, eyelet punch and spare sail cloth.

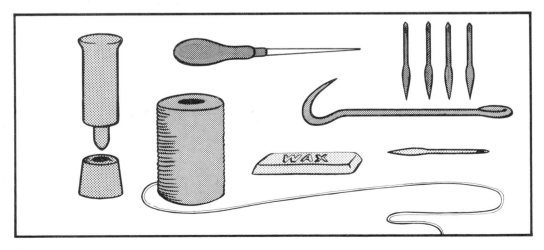

Tears

Use a hook to tension the sail, with the tear pointing at you. Thread the needle and knot the end of the twine. Bring the needle up through the cloth just to the left of the end of the tear furthest away. Pass the needle down to the right and then bring it up through the tear on the far side of the first stitch. The second stitch is started by passing the needle down through the tear and up through the cloth just to its left, then continue as for the first. Use just enough tension to bring the edges together. Any grandmother will tell you that this is darning, but sailors refer to it as the herring-bone stitch.

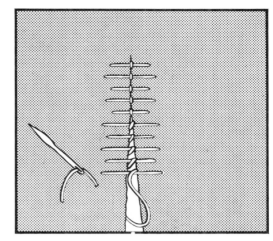

Patching

The size of the patch should be such that when its corners have been mitred and about ½in (12mm) of 'hem' have been turned in, it will overlap the damaged area by about 2in (50mm) all round. The hem can be made to stay by rubbing it firmly with a fid or any other smooth object. Locate the patch in position and tack the four corners, then sew it with a flat seam. Turn the sail over and cut away the damage, leaving about 1½in (35mm) all round the patch stitching. Cut across the corners to allow ½in (12mm) to be turned under, then sew it with a flat seam.

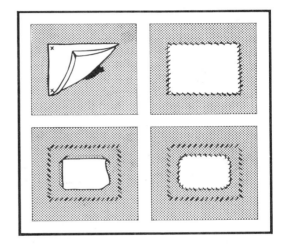

Roping

Fibre bolt ropes not inside the tabling often need restitching or 'roping'. The edge of the sail should be towards you with the hook holding the work out to the right. Pass the needle with knotted twine under one strand of the rope and up through the sail. Lead the twine along the contline, pass the needle under the next strand, and so on.

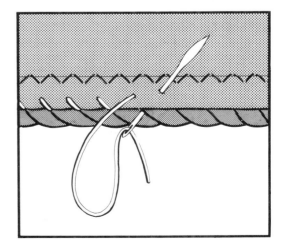

Sails

Seams

When seam stitching has chafed, it is best to restitch it with a flat seam, following the original holes. In fact, this will reproduce half of the machine stitch. Hand stitching is usually so much stronger than machine that this half will suffice, but the other half could be completed by going over the work again.

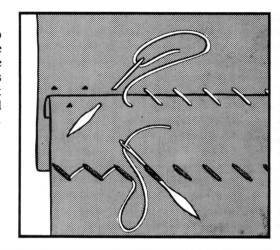

Punched Eye

On small sails, a hole is cut in the cloth, the tubular collar is passed through it and the end spread over the flat washer on the other side, using a die. Punched eyes might also be used on awnings where no great strain is expected.

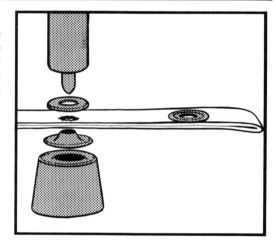

Worked Eye

If any real strain is expected, this is the eye to use. The basis is a brass ring and this is offered up to the cloth and its inner and outer circumferences traced on the cloth with a pencil. Across the inner of these two, two slits are cut at right angles to each other. The needle, threaded with knotted twine, is passed down through the cloth outside of the ring and brought up inside. The stitches should be close together and, so far as is possible, cover the ring completely. For maximum strength, use the twine quadrupled, wax it well and prick holes in the cloth before attempting to pass the needle through it. These worked eyes are often used at the corners of sails which have been rein-

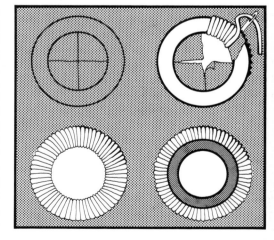

orced with extra layers of cloth. The stitches
are protected from the chafe of shackles, or
whatever by inserting a liner with an appropriate punch and die.

Cringle

This is an eye made of fibre rope which
finishes up outside of the sail. A start is made
by working two eyes in the required position.
Take a single strand of rope about four times
the diameter of the finished cringle. Pass an
end through one of the eyes and adjust it so
that one-third of its length is one side of the
sail and two-thirds the other. Lay up the
shorter end around the longer, following the
original lay. Pass the longer end through the
second eye and lay this up with the other two
strands. Each end should now be passed
through an eye and tucked into the lay of the
cringle which has now been formed. The
finished cringle should be of such a size that
it will need stretching with a fid before the
thimble can be hammered in. This thimble
should be forced in from the same side as the
cloth to avoid fouling it. The tighter the fit,

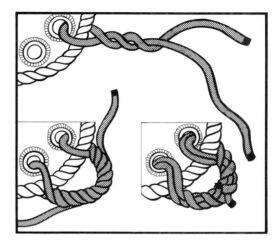

the better. An alternative for the more proficient is to splice in the thimble directly, but
it is more difficult to get a snug fit this way.

Sails

Slides

Sew a length of tape to the slide and then pass the end of the tape through the eye in the sail, back through the eye and round again as many times as is a comfortable fit. Sew right through all the thicknesses of tape and cut off the surplus.

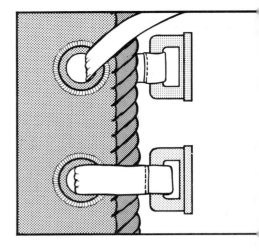

Luff Rope

If a luff rope has been renewed, apart from restitching the tabling, it will be necessary to lash the head and tack of the sail to each e at the end of the luff rope.

Engines

very engine should have its own handbook manual in which will be specified the aintenance schedule. In addition it will obably have a 'Trouble Shooting Chart' hich will include more remedial suggestions an most owners would care to put into actice. However, the manufacturers of gines often make no reference to the uipment to which the engine is coupled, so addition to considering faults concerned ith the engine itself, it is worth looking at ose of the associated equipment.

The improvising of tools for work on an gine is seldom successful and a good tool t is essential if even day-to-day work is to undertaken.

Engines are considered as falling into ree general groups, diesel, petrol and tboard.

iesel

he diesel engine is better suited to a marine vironment than petrol if only because of e absence of an electrical ignition system. amp conditions will not prevent a diesel gine starting when the petrol equivalent is manding lots of drying attention. The fety factor of a less inflammable fuel is other point in its favour, but weight and st go part way towards balancing the ales. However, what is of immediate ncern is the maintenance of all types of gine, and in that respect it is fair to say at the only major differences are in the stribution of fuel and the way in which it is nited. The differences, such as they are, ll be considered in the appropriate ntext.

r Filters

ll types of engine rely on a mixture of fuel d air to drive them. The air is filtered to ep foreign bodies out of the engine and the filters will, in time, need cleaning and changing. If of the dry paper element type, the element can be removed, cleaned free of dust and replaced. It will need replacing when either it is physically damaged or the pores are clogged with oily dust.

Another type of filter is the oil bath type. A fine mesh holds a reservoir of oil through which the air is filtered. This type should never need renewing, but the oil should be changed occasionally. Immerse the filter in diesel fuel or paraffin and clean it thoroughly, then submerge it in new engine oil for a few minutes. Allow all the surplus oil to drip off, wipe it clean and replace.

Engine Oil

The level of the oil in the engine should be checked before starting the engine each day. In addition, at the prescribed intervals, it should be changed, as should its filters. Unlike those in cars, marine engine sumps rarely allow the oil to be drained by gravity – it is normal to pump it out. Some engines have fixed pumps; others will need a portable one with an inlet pipe of such a diameter that it can be introduced into the sump by way of the dipstick hole. In the absence of a special wrench, the filter can be removed by driving a screwdriver through the side and using that as a lever. Before driving the screwdriver in, make sure there is a new filter available and that there is a container ready to catch the oil which will leak out. When the new filter has been replaced and new oil added up to the correct level on the dipstick, run the engine, checking for an oil leak around the filter and that the oil pressure is normal. After a few minutes, stop the engine and check the oil level again.

Other oils which require checking and changing at the scheduled intervals are those in the gearbox, reduction box and injection pump cambox.

Fuel System

Diesel engines are very fussy about the cleanliness of the fuel they use. The merest hint of water, dirt or air and the engine will stop. At the bottom of the fuel tank should be a trap to collect water and other rubbish. You should drain this frequently, having first turned off the cock above it, and not forgetting to turn that cock on again.

Between the fuel tank and the engine will often be found one, if not two, bulkhead mounted water traps. If the glass bowl contains anything other than pure, clean diesel fuel, it should be removed and the contents disposed of. An advantage of two bulkhead mounted traps is that either one can normally be isolated and emptied while the engine is running.

The next stage in the fuel system is the fuel lift pump. This often contains a diaphragm and a gauze filter. The diaphragm is an essential component; if it is split the pump will not work and consequently the engine will not run. If present, the gauze filter should be clean.

After the pump, the fuel is passed through one or two filters, the elements of which need changing periodically. This element might be an insert to a removable bowl, or take the form of a complete cartridge which screws on to a top plate. If of the former type, clean the bowl thoroughly before replacing the new element.

The injection pump is the diesel engine's equivalent of the carburettor. It takes clean fuel from the filters and at precisely the opportune moment to allow for complete ignition, it injects a measured quantity into the injectors. The injectors spray the fuel into the cylinders, where it is compressed, and the resulting rapid rise in temperature causes it to ignite. The amateur would be well advised to limit his adjusting of pumps and injectors to the following. The throttle cable is attached to the pump and it is with part of this fitting that the slow running speed of the engine can be adjusted.

Each injector should be inspected occasionally, for which purpose it will have to be removed from the cylinder. It will be found that there are two fuel pipes associated with each injector. One is the feed from the pump, the other returns the surplus fuel to the tank. Both must be disconnected. The injector itself is normally held in place with a flange and two nuts. If there is a build up of carbon on the spray tip of the injector it will need cleaning. The most reliable way of performing that task is to take or send it to a manufacturer such as Lucas-CAV. The injector is a very precise piece of equipment and the poking of lengths of wire up the holes which make the spray will achieve nothing but harm.

One of the few liabilities of a diesel engine is its absolute insistence on pure fuel. This means that when any part of the fuel system has been disturbed, and sometimes even when it has not, the engine will not run reliably until all the air in the pipes has been expelled. This venting or bleeding of the fuel system is normally required to follow a precise and logical pattern, opening and closing a series of vent screws on the fuel filters and the injection pump, while pumping fuel through by operating the fuel pump manually.

Any one screw is left open until there is no trace of air bubbles in the fuel emitting from its hole, whereupon the screw is tightened and the next in sequence slackened. It is imperative for every diesel engine user to know how to expel air from his engine in the approved manner, for it is the only way which can be relied on for long periods. However, there is a quicker way which has saved more than one potentially embarrassing situation resulting from unexpected engine failure. It entails going straight to the injection pump and slackening just the higher of the two vent screws. With a normally inclined engine, this will be the forward one. The gears and throttle are set for normal starting and the engine turned over with the starting motor. When the engine starts, tighten the vent screw and carry on with your business. This is a method which should be used in an emergency only, and remember to bleed the whole system properly at a more opportune moment. In anticipation of such an emergency, it is worth allocating one spanner to this task alone and wrapping it up in the large rag necessary to absorb the copious quantities of fuel which will be ejected.

One final point concerning the bleeding of

engines in the conventional manner is the operation of the fuel pump. When being driven by the engine, it is worked on a cam. If, when the engine stops, the cam is at the top of its stroke, no amount of operating of the hand lever will achieve the pumping of fuel. The answer is to 'touch' the starter button just enough to move the cam.

The level of the cooling water should be checked each day before starting the engine and if it requires frequent topping up it will be as well to check all the pipe clips for security. The water in a cooling system is normally discoloured, if only owing to the presence of antifreeze, and it is not usually difficult to find where the water is leaking.

Within the scope of the average mariner should also be the checking and adjusting of the tension of the drive belt. It drives both generator and water pump, so a change in the efficiency of either, as indicated by a lower rate of charging or a higher engine running temperature, could be attributable to a slack drive belt. It is tightened by pivoting the generator around the lower of the three bolts which secure it. Mounted just

below the exhaust manifold, as it usually is, its adjustment is made with less discomfort when the engine is cold. That reason alone is sufficient to justify checking the tension of the belt when the engine is cold.

An accumulation of fine black dust near and around the generator area is a sign that the belt is being worn. This does not necessarily indicate a slack belt; it could mean that the pulleys around which the belt run are not aligned correctly. The rectification of that is not a simple job and is one best left to an engineer.

Overheating

Engines are cooled by either a direct or indirect system. In the former, the 'sea' water is pumped around the engine to keep it cool. In the latter, the engine is cooled by a closed circuit of fresh water which, in its turn, is cooled by the sea water. In either case, there is a sea water inlet to the boat. The inlet consists of a cock by which the water is turned on or off and a strainer which filters it. Particularly at times of spring tides, when the weed and flotsam which accumulate at

the high-water tide mark is washed into the estuaries, water strainers tend to become blocked. A blocked strainer is usually diagnosed by a shortage of water being ejected with the exhaust. Alternative causes, as mentioned earlier, could be a shortage of fresh water in the closed system or a slack drive belt.

If the engine is overheating and a blocked strainer is the likely fault, as soon as it is reasonably possible, stop the engine. Then turn off the seacock at the base of the strainer body. Access to the mesh strainer itself is by way of the cover at the top. It is usually held down with two wing nuts, both of which should be slackened, but neither removed completely. A slot in the cover, adjacent to one of the nuts, allows it to be turned to one side to facilitate removal of the strainer. By this time, it is almost inevitable that your hands will be greasy, so it is much safer to clean the removed strainer in a bucket, rather than by leaning over the side. The contents, normally weed and crustaceans, are poked out with a screwdriver, care being taken to avoid damaging the mesh.

When all the obstructions have been removed and the fitting reassembled, turn on the seacock and check for water leaks before starting the engine.

Stern Gland

Part of the lubrication of the propeller drive shaft is by means of an adjustable stern gland. The adjustment, normally effected by two nuts acting on a flange, is to compress the packing in the gland in order to extract its grease to lubricate the shaft and keep the water out. The packing is a grease-impregnated fibre, square in cross-section. Lengths are wrapped around the shaft and pushed well into the gland. As many lengths as possible are added, the limit being when the flange and nuts can just be replaced. The time to renew the packing is either when the nuts are at the limit of their adjustment or the gland leaks water in spite of adjustment.

Remove the nuts and slide the flange forward along the shaft. A thin, rigid hook is needed to remove the old packing, which always shows a natural reluctance to come out. New, the packing is of a square cross-

section; after use it is distorted. It is important to use the correct size, which can be found by measuring the gland rather than the old packing.

When offering up the new packing, cut mitred joints so that it makes a snug fit all round the shaft, then push it well in. Add as many more lengths as are necessary to fill the gland, staggering the joins around the shaft. Finally, with a certain amount of difficulty if you have put in enough lengths of packing, refit the flange and nuts.

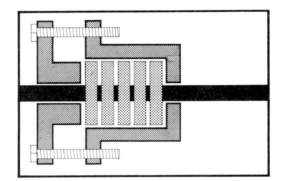

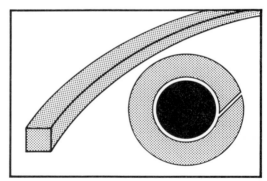

Vibration

Any change in the vibration of the engine should be investigated immediately. Though it is often a result of a mechanical fault in the engine itself or loose holding-down bolts, it is frequently as a result of the propeller being out of balance. This can be caused by hitting a floating object and bending or, worse still, removing a part of a blade. Hitting flotsam is often unavoidable, but all other causes of propeller damage such as electrolysis or bad boat handling should be eradicated. Small dents and knocks can often be corrected with

judicious use of a wrench and a fine file, but larger scale damage will require the attention of a professional.

Petrol

Most of the mechanics of the petrol engine are very similar to those of the diesel. The major exceptions are the fuel and ignition systems.

Fuel

Though not quite as fussy as diesel, petrol engines still appreciate good, clean fuel. It will normally be filtered at least once before arriving at the carburettor, the mixing and distribution point for the air and petrol. The passageways within the carburettor are, of necessity, quite narrow, and they themselves incorporate further restrictions in the form of removable 'jets'. Relatively small foreign bodies can cause obstructions resulting in

either reduced performance or even complete engine failure. The variety of carburettors in use is so great as to make it impracticable to discuss them all in detail, information which will be in the engine handbook or manual, anyway. Suffice to say that the owner ought to be able to remove, clean and replace the carburettor jets.

The flow of fuel through the carburettor is controlled by a float actuating a tapered needle in an orifice, the result of which is either to allow the fuel to flow or to stop it. If the float jams, which it is prone to do occasionally, the result is a flooded carburettor. Not only will this affect the performance but it is highly dangerous. The immediate action required is to turn off the supply of petrol and then investigate the float chamber.

Ignition

Unlike diesel engines, which rely on the heat

generated by compressing the fuel to ignite it, petrol engines rely on an electric spark. This high voltage spark is produced from the low voltage battery in the coil and passed on to the distributor which offers it to each of the spark plugs in turn. The spark plugs are mounted in each cylinder and start the ignition of the fuel.

The passage of the spark causes wear, not only on the plugs, but also on a pair of 'points' in the distributor. It should be part of routine maintenance to remove the plugs and points and clean them with a wire brush for the former and an oil stone for the latter. The gap of each plug should be set before replacing it, and the gap between the points must be set when they are in position.

If the engine will not start, it is often owing to moisture on the ignition leads. All the exposed parts should be dried by wiping with a clean, dry cloth, or by spraying with an aerosol oil.

Outboard

Petrol engines are lighter than diesel, which makes them better suited to portable use. The result is a susceptibility to ignition problems, just like the inboard petrol engines, only more so owing to the inevitably exposed position.

Of unique concern to the owner of an outboard engine is the fault known as 'dropping it in the water'. This is likely to happen when the engine is being put in the boat or taken out, but it might also occur when in use. If it is not securely mounted on the transom, when turning sharply the force of the propeller can twist the engine off. With luck, the safety line will keep it in contact with the boat. If it happens like that, the engine will have been running when it hit the water and the cylinder will, inevitably, be full of water. The alternative case of dunking it when it was not running is only marginally better. In either case, immediate remedial action is essential.

Hose and wash the entire motor and all its parts with clean fresh water, removing all signs of salt, mud and any other foreign bodies. Wipe off the surplus water.

Take out the spark plug and remove the carburettor, then operate the manual starter

rapidly and frequently. The water within should be ejected.

Fill the cylinder with oil by way of the spark plug hole, then operate the manual starter slowly. The object of this is to spread the oil around as much as possible. Drain off the surplus oil.

Clean, dry and replace the spark plugs.

Wash the carburettor thoroughly by agitating it in clean petrol. Make sure that it is completely immersed and that there are no naked flames. Replace the carburettor.

If the fuel tank went under water, empty it and wash out with clean petrol before refilling it.

Start the engine and run it at low speed until it reaches normal operating temperature, then take it for a run until it is thoroughly dry.

If at any stage the engine will not turn over easily, or if it will not run as well as it did before the dunking, it will need dismantling and more intimate attention.

Inhibiting

If an engine is not to be used for a prolonged period, perhaps over a winter, it will be as well to lay it up properly and so minimise the problems when trying to start it later. The first stage, regardless of type of engine, is to complete a full service, including lubrication, oils and filter changes.

Outboards

Run the engine in clean fresh water for five minutes to purge the waterways of corrosive salt. How this is achieved will be solved by ingenuity and with care. A 45 gallon drum can be of use, but beware the propeller hitting the side. Whatever the solution, make sure the mounting is strong and rigid. An airborne running outboard engine sounds indescribably dangerous and incredibly expensive.

When the water system is clean, increase the engine speed to normal cruising and use a pump oil can to squirt an inhibiting oil into the air intake. Turn off the fuel supply and keep injecting the oil until the engine finally comes to rest.

The best storage conditions will be warm and dry – a corner of the sitting room would probably be ideal. Mount the engine upright, preferably on a purpose-built stand to keep the weight off the skeg. A cover will only encourage condensation, so leave it open to the air. Cover all the orifices, such as air intake and exhaust outlet, with combinations of polythene sheet, masking tape and string, to keep out moist air. Finally, wipe all exposed surfaces with an oily rag.

Inboards

If the water-cooling system is 'closed', that is, if it is recirculating fresh water, drain it and refill with fresh water and antifreeze. If sea water or other raw water is used for cooling, flush the system well with clean fresh water. This might be achieved by disconnecting a pipe on the suction side of the water pump and replacing it with one long enough to reach to the bottom of an adjacent bucket. Flush the engine with several bucketsful, adding half a cup of a soluble oil to the last. Never run the engine dry or the water pump impeller will disintegrate.

Inject inhibiting oil into each cylinder by way of the spark plug or injector holes and turn the engine over slowly, preferably by hand, to spread it around. Add more inhibiting oil, sufficient to cover the top of the pistons. Seal the holes with old spark plugs or injectors.

Once again, seal off all the orifices with polythene sheet. Wash the engine clean with warm soapy water and, when it is dry, brush or spray it with a thin film of oil.

Even if the engine service specification omitted to mention it, lubricate thoroughly all controls, cables and linkages.

Starting

Remove all tape, string and polythene sheet. Remove any drain plugs to release condensation which beat the system. Check that all plugs and cocks are in the correct operating position. Replace new plugs or reconditioned injectors. Check all oil levels, engage gear and turn the engine over slowly by hand. Fill the fuel tank, prime the pump and start the engine. Check that the cooling water is running and finally use paraffin to clean the engine free of oil. While doing that, look out for water and fuel leaks.

10 Electrics

To many boat owners, electrics are more of a mystery than the universe itself, though heaven only knows why. Poor electrics are the bane of every sailor and every effort ought to be made to maintain them in the best possible condition. The low voltage system used in most craft – usually 12 or 24 volts – is not particularly dangerous, and it will respond to a little attention and respect.

Batteries

If correctly installed with retaining straps in a well-ventilated position, the ordinary lead-acid or 'car' battery should require little maintenance. Check regularly the level of the electrolyte and if necessary fill it up to just above the plates with distilled water. For this it is best to use a plastic pourer which will not be adversely affected if acid is accidentally splashed on it. Purpose-made bottles are the ideal, but with the right technique a washing-up-liquid bottle can be used. The potential problem is the spilling of water on to the battery as the bottle is offered up. If it is squeezed while still vertical it will expel air, and if released while being tipped, the air returning to the bottle will prevent the water escaping. The process can be reversed to remove the bottle.

The time to add water is just before charging the battery, particularly if the ambient temperature is anywhere near freezing. When mixed with the acid in the battery the water will not freeze at normal air temperatures and the only way to be sure that it is well mixed is by charging. Having added the water, replace the vent caps, ensuring that the holes in them are not blocked. But resist the temptation to blow through them because the acid will do you no good at all.

Clean and dry the battery top and sides with a disposable cloth – any acid it mig absorb will not be welcome elsewhere.

Using a wire brush if necessary, remo any sign of corrosion from the terminals, b be careful to avoid making an electrical co nection between them and something else means of the wire bristles. Check t terminals for tightness and then smear the with petroleum jelly. If the topping up a cleaning is performed every week while t boat is in commission, the battery shou function satisfactorily as long as it is ke charged.

Voltage readings, whether from one of t boat's own instruments or from a mo sophisticated portable type, will not nece sarily tell an accurate tale about the state charge of the battery. On open circuit, th is, when the battery terminal connectio have been removed or isolated, a low volta certainly indicates a low state of charge, b

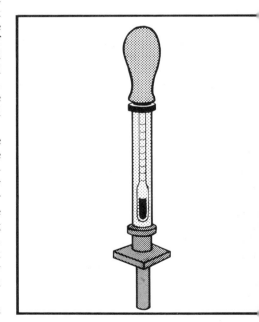

high voltage does not necessarily indicate that the battery is in good condition. The most reliable indication of the state of charge is the specific gravity of the electrolyte. This can be measured easily with a hydrometer, an inexpensive item of equipment well worth having on board. A sample of the electrolyte is sucked up into a glass tube, where there is a glass float. The figure of the level at which it floats in the electrolyte indicates the specific gravity. The warmer the electrolyte, the more it expands and the less dense it becomes, so for an accurate indication of the state of the battery the temperature of the electrolyte is also needed. Before charging it will probably be at air temperature, but after it will be higher. The following table will give an indication of the sort of figures to be expected.

Hydrometer Readings

Condition of cell	Temperature							
	50°F (10°C)	59°F (15°C)	68°F (20°C)	77°F (25°C)	86°F (30°C)	95°F (35°C)	104°F (40°C)	113°F (45°C)
Fully charged	1.288	1.284	1.281	1.277	1.273	1.270	1.266	1.262
Half charged	1.208	1.204	1.201	1.197	1.193	1.190	1.186	1.182
Fully discharged	1.118	1.114	1.111	1.107	1.103	1.100	1.096	1.092

When not in use, batteries should be isolated from all circuits by means of a switch or, failing that, by removing both terminal connections. This will prevent any possible electrolytic action. Note that when the engine is running the battery can be considered to be in use and so should never be isolated.

Charging

When a battery is not well charged, the voltage on which it will be working will be low and a light bulb run off it will be correspondingly dim. If the engine is started and the charging circuit works, the bulb will get brighter, indicating an increase in voltage across the battery terminal connections – a necessary requirement for recharging the battery. Such an increase in voltage when the engine is running with no corresponding charging of the battery could be due either to poor battery terminal connections or a failure of the battery itself.

Disconnect the battery leads and clean them with emery cloth until they shine. Do the same with the terminals; apply a smear of petroleum jelly to them and reconnect the leads. Tap on the terminals firmly with a wooden mallet or the handle of a hammer before tightening the screws or nuts. If the leads are removed one at a time, there will be little chance of reconnecting them incorrectly.

When the battery is fully charged, the running of the engine will not necessarily increase the brightness of a bulb because the battery voltage might be very close to that of the generator, so the above observation can only be made if the battery is known to be lacking in charge. In this case, if there is no change in the brightness of a light bulb, the indication is that no extra volts are arriving at the battery. This could be due to poor electrical connections on the generator itself. With the engine stationary, remove the connection from the generator and clean it. The negative side of the battery will be connected to the engine by means of an engine holding down bolt or a similar substantial one elsewhere, perhaps on the generator itself. Remove this second connection, clean it and replace it.

If there is still no sign of charging and the drive belt is intact and tight, the fault probably lies within the generator itself. If the lack of charging was a sudden happening, or if the generator is an alternator, the safe solution is to consult a qualified engineer. Alternators are not only fragile, but expensive to repair.

If the fault developed gradually and the

generator is a dynamo, it will be possible to check the condition of the carbon brushes. It is probable that they will be worn to the point of being useless. Reference to the handbook will indicate which type of charging system is fitted to the engine and, if appropriate, will give guidance towards removing the brushes.

Wiring

When renewing wiring, with one or two provisos, be guided by both the size and type of that being removed. The major part of all boat wiring is with twin-core wire, though there are occasions when three-core is useful, such as for two-way switching of domestic lighting or for lights up a mast.

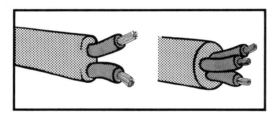

The smaller the cross-sectional area of electrical wire, the greater will be its resistance to the passage of current. The greater its resistance, the greater will be the voltage drop along its length. Since the object of electric wiring is to convey power from the battery to an appliance, it follows that the bigger the wire, the more efficiently it will be conveyed. Increasing the size of wire could mean brighter lights and faster pumps. If that in use previously was dangerously small, it might also mean cooler and safer wiring. Added to that, there is no increase in power consumption. Of course, if an appliance is performing satisfactorily, there is little to be gained by investing extra money in unnecessarily large wire.

Single-stranded 'cable' is intended to be fixed rigidly. The single strand will break with a minimum of flexing and so is unsuitable for small boats where some movement is regarded as normal. Much better suited is a multi-strand wire which can be subjected to a degree of flexing without danger of breaking.

So far as is possible, all wiring should be run in straight lines and be well supported with screwed saddles. If the saddles are nailed, not only are they more likely to fall away, but the act of hammering in the nails might lead to damage of the wire or its covering.

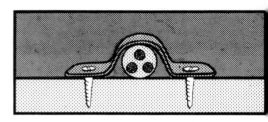

The cause of failure of most wire is either the breakdown of the insulation or corrosion of the ends. The first can be overcome, more or less permanently, by replacing it with wire of modern manufacture. The second cannot be avoided completely, but its effect can be minimised when rewiring by allowing extra length to enable the terminal fittings to be remade occasionally without the need for rewiring again. An allowance of 2in (50mm) for each end means that, for an investment in an extra 40in (1m) of wire, the terminal connections can be remade ten times and in so doing save the cost of a new length of wire. Of course, it would be possible to overcome that problem by joining in short lengths, but every join is a potential open circuit and should be avoided if at all possible. The ideal would be unbroken runs from distribution board to the appliance. Any joins there are should be made with screw connectors and bound with waterproof insulating tape. Twisting the ends together is not a very efficient way of joining wires.

Sooner or later drops of condensation will form on the wire and as the boat rolls, they will run along it. If left unchecked, the water will enter the nearest fitting and initiate corrosion at the terminals. This will result eventually in a need to remake the terminals but not only that, it is possible that the whole fitting will have to be replaced. The problem can be overcome by putting a U-bend in the wire just before it enters the fitting. This will serve to trap the drops which can then be wiped away.

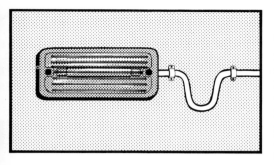

Wires are particularly vulnerable where they pass through bulkheads, and care should be taken to avoid fracturing the outer sheath. The copper wire strands which make up the electrical conductor will last indefinitely if protected from moisture and will corrode very quickly if not. At these vulnerable points, use rubber grommets, or at least several turns of insulating tape, as a permanent protection.

For wires which pass through the deck, it is preferable to have a plug and socket arrangement. This will allow the mast to be removed without cutting the wire. The waterproof screw-type is best, and it has its own screw-on cover for use when the plug is not in. If a plug and socket is not used, the minimum requirement is for a waterproof gland through which to pass the wire. These are not always as effective as would be desirable and often need the addition of a silicon rubber compound to be made watertight.

Lighting

With the exception of the engine starter motor which demands an enormous amount of current and the radio transmitter which has its own special requirement, all the electrical circuits should be protected by fuses or circuit breakers which are normally mounted on a communal distribution board. Each appliance or fitting will usually have its own fuse, and a fault on that circuit does not affect any other. However, it is quite common to have one lighting circuit for all the boat's domestic needs. What this means is that if the fuse blows for any reason, the whole boat can be plunged into darkness. It is more practicable to have two lighting circuits arranged in such a way that if one fails, the lights from the other will supply sufficient illumination to move about in safety. One way of organising that is to have one side of the boat on one fuse and the other on another. Navigation and deck lights should be fed, of course, from their own completely separate fuses.

Electronics

As more and more electronic equipment appears on board boats, and elsewhere for that matter, it is conceivable that in time the amateur mariner will become sufficiently familiar with it as to be able to effect minor repairs on very much the same scale as he does now to, say, the engine. To most of us, however, it will remain the dark side of technology. The extent of our maintenance will be to ensure an adequate supply of electricity and to keep it dry.

The supply of power might be from the boat's battery or from internal dry batteries which will need replacing periodically. Between replacements it is worth the occasional look to make sure they are not leaking the corrosive contents.

The watertightness of electronic equipment is of paramount importance and every effort should be made to keep it so. All seals and grommets should be inspected regularly for signs of water getting inside the box. Silicon rubber compounds can be used to good effect as extra seals around removable backs, lids and entrance holes for wires.

If kept dry, the actual circuitry needs nothing further to protect it. Though superbly useful for other applications, the use of aerosol spray-on oil can, by all accounts, do much more harm than good to electronic circuitry. Its use is a constant cause of failure of printed circuit boards. It is much more productive to endeavour to keep moisture out of the case in the first place and use silica gel to absorb any that beats the system.

As stated earlier, a radio transmitter is an exception to the rule of feeding all electrical appliances from fuses on a central distribution board. Since one of its uses is for communication in times of emergency, it would be as well if it could be organised in such a way that it would be one of the later pieces of equipment to fail. For that reason, it should be connected directly to the battery, then if a disaster immobilises the other electrics, there is still a chance of the radio working. It will still need to be protected by fuses and in this case they should be line fuses, that is, one in each of the leads. If they are fitted in opposite directions, there can be no chance of reversing the polarity of the volts offered to the transmitter, should the supply have been disconnected for any reason.

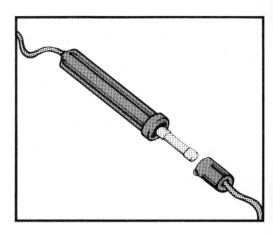

11 Plumbing

The primary object of boating is to move through the water, but it is sometimes a revelation to consider how much moving about of water within the boat is a necessary adjunct to this pursuit. This water falls into three distinct categories. The first is concerned with sea water which, on demand, we expect to arrive, flush the heads and go away again. The second is concerned with fresh water which we need for cooking and personal hygiene. The third concerns the unwanted water in the bilge.

Sea Water

This can be taken to mean the water, 'sea' or 'fresh' in which the boat is floating. A source of this water can be used to flush the heads, when in a socially acceptable area to do so, or for general use about the boat such as deck cleaning or fire-fighting. Because it will be collected through a hole in the hull, it is essential that the fitting which will allow that to happen can also be used to turn off the supply when it is not required or would otherwise be unwelcome. That fitting is the seacock.

Seacocks

These can be used either to allow water in or to allow its passage out. A heads, for example, needs an inlet for flushing purposes and an outlet for discharging the waste. Both will be mounted below the water line, the first of necessity, the second for social reasons. It is because they are mounted below the water line that it is imperative that they are kept in working order. As long as the piping and fittings are sound, all will be well, but the failure of one hose clip or the fracturing of one pipe can lead to frantic activity if the seacock will not budge.

Proper seacocks are those which have a tapered cone fitting and can be turned off or on by simply moving the handle through 90°. The screw gate valve-type, similar to a domestic tap, will do the job, but is more likely to get blocked.

Apart from the relative size, the outlet being larger, the only difference of principle of inlet and outlet seacocks is the presence or absence of a grill on the outside of the hull. It is desirable to filter the water on its way in, but not so when it is being discharged. This grill is a great attraction to small crustaceans and when access to the bottom is available, it is worth having a prod at them with a spike or electrical screwdriver.

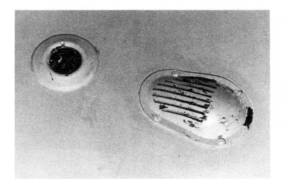

While the boat is high and dry is also the time to dismantle the seacock. Just below the handle is a flange which is held in position by a pair of nuts and set screws. With these removed, the handle and cone can be withdrawn. If it is not well greased, it might take a little working of the handle while exerting upward pressure on it. Wipe the cone free of grease and rub it lightly with emery cloth to remove any corrosion. Do the same to the fitting, using the handle of a screwdriver perhaps, to get well into it, then apply a liberal coating of waterproof grease or a special seacock grease, and reassemble it. The handle can be mounted in four different positions, so if it comes off, make sure it is replaced in the right manner.

Pipes

In modern small craft, piping is virtually exclusively of polythene or other plastic derivative. The relative ease with which such pipes can be fitted and made to take up awkward shapes is an invaluable asset, but it can lead to collapsing walls and consequent constrictions, so be careful on that score. When fitting a new pipe to a seacock which is below the water line, lead it in an arc so that its highest point is above sea level. This will minimise the chances of water rushing in if the pipe comes off the heads. If polythene pipes are expected to handle water under pressure, which is the case when it is pumped, they will be less likely to collapse if of the reinforced variety.

The fitting of polythene pipe over fittings usually necessitates making it more supple by applying heat. This must be done by an indirect means such as by dipping the end in a mug of hot water. The application of direct heat with a burner, no matter how gentle the intention, will result in a sticky mess and an end of pipe that needs retrimming.

Clips No matter how much of a struggle it was to get the pipe on, do not be lulled into thinking it will show as much resistance to falling off. A securing clip is essential. The worm-drive type made of stainless steel is probably the best available today. The final word about clips is to remember to put them on the pipe before putting the pipe on the fitting!

Heads

Non-discharging heads are becoming more popular as conscience and legislation make us more aware of the world outside of the boat. There are those with removable tanks which can be taken ashore and disposed of in a toilet and there are those in which the waste can be sealed in a polythene bag for discreet disposal. However, for the present, since there is no plumbing involved, we will ignore the modern and consider only the more traditional heads. These are available in a variety of shapes, sizes and efficiencies. Some rely on the action of one pump to both flush and evacuate the bowl; others use separate pumps.

The Blake's Lavac is one which uses just one pump and that is the only part of it which will ever require servicing. The pump will be discussed in a later section.

Those heads which have separate pumps – and they are still in a large majority – use those which are very simple and consequently very reliable. I refer to the lift pump. If such a pump fails suddenly, it is almost certainly owing to the failure of one of the valves and that is just as certainly because it is jammed in the wrong position by a foreign body. The only answer is to dismantle the pump, remove the obstruction and reassemble it. That is an unpleasant task, best performed by the most recent user.

Provided it is used in the intended manner and not asked to dispose of items which have not passed through the body (other than paper) it is more likely that the type of fault will be quite different. In time, the various seals will need replacing, warning of which will be given by the pump concerned starting to leak. In this case, the heads can be pumped well clean before dismantling, and the task takes on a whole new aura. Manufacturers will supply kits containing all washers and seals necessary to recondition their heads and this is worth doing once each year in an attempt to avoid problems when in commission.

The extent of day-to-day maintenance could be the pumping of the washing-up water through the system. Soap or detergent is the best lubricant. Apart from that, the shafts of the lift pumps will need occasional lubrication by means of the grease caps and they themselves will need refilling with waterproof grease.

Fresh Water

Water for consumption, whether directly or in the cooking, must be carried on board. This might be in portable containers, but most boats will have a water 'system' consisting of a tank, pipes and pump. If the system is not kept reasonably clean, the result could be at best a degree of discomfort, at worst, a serious illness. It is worthwhile ensuring that the water which comes from the pump is fit for human consumption.

Tanks

Water being a very heavy commodity, the tank is normally located in a position where it will have least effect on the trim and stability of the boat. Undoubtedly, the most suitable position is under the sole in the saloon or, failing that, two tanks, one under each of the saloon settee bunks. An often used alternative, presumably because the other two locations are unavailable, is beneath the cockpit. This can only be considered a good position if there really is no alternative.

Older tanks were made of riveted galvanised steel and have given, indeed still are giving, good service. All tanks should have an inspection cover large enough to allow the most remote corners of the tank to be cleaned. The covers on steel tanks are often secured and made watertight with numerous nuts and bolts. Larger tanks will have a baffle plate to reduce the movement of water within the tank as the boat rolls, but this can be an inconvenience when it comes to cleaning.

Once a year the tank should be emptied completely and thoroughly cleaned and all the debris which somehow finds its way there should be removed. When it is clean, both inside and out, give it a close inspection, particularly along the seams and at the corners, looking for any sign of rust. Sooner or later it will be found. If no better way is available, wire brush all the rust away, inside and out, and then clean the tank out again. The outside can be protected with paint, as may the inside, but until modern epoxy paints became available, a cement wash was considered the best finish.

Before painting, it will be worth checking the inlet and outlet fittings for security, particularly if rust is in abundant evidence elsewhere.

Tanks made of GRP are becoming more and more common. The first taste of water from one might make the casual observer ask why. Fortunately, the 'plastic' taste diminishes as the tank is used and eventually it becomes quite acceptable. A natural resistance to corrosion and no treatment being required, other than annual cleaning, goes even further towards making GRP tanks acceptable. The most common structural fault with GRP tanks seems to be the top-to-side bonding and this often needs repairing with a fibreglass paste.

Flexible tanks, made of neoprene or other plastic, will make more efficient use of a given volume than the rigid alternatives. Though often used as the only tank on board, they are particularly useful as a means of temporarily increasing the carrying capacity for a specific voyage. The biggest problem is the chafe which is easily caused by their rolling when partially full. This can be minimised by storing them in a V-shaped locker where the natural tendency will be for the tank to slip to the bottom and so reduce the rolling effect.

Pipes

As with salt-water feeds, nearly all piping is derived from polythene or plastic. Apart from the relative ease of fitting, it avoids any galvanic action. Each rigid tank will have three pipes to it: an inlet, an outlet and a vent. Because they collapse as the water is withdrawn, flexible tanks have no need of a vent.

The inlet pipe will normally be led, as a convenience, from a deck fitting. This pipe will be of a large bore and led as directly as possible to avoid 'blow backs'.

A vent pipe is necessary, theoretically, to allow air to be released from a rigid tank as the water gushes in. Presumably for reasons of economy, this pipe is often of such a small bore as to be incapable of venting air at a rate to match that at which the water can be forced in. If the pressure behind the water is sufficiently high, it is possible to 'inflate' a rigid tank, often to the detriment of its seams if it is of galvanised steel. Pumps of the lift and diaphragm principles of operation will allow water to pass and increase the apparent venting. These two types are those most commonly used as manual pumps, but they may also be used as part of a pressurised system, in which case opening the taps will increase the venting even more. The pumps and taps can also give a timely warning of the tank being full, just before water overflows from the vent tube.

The outlet fitting will incorporate a gate-valve type of stop cock, yet another the free operation of which it would be as well to ensure by dismantling and lubricating each year. If there is a pressurised-water system, there should be a branch immediately after the outlet valve leading to two other valves, one for the pressurised system, the other for the manual. Not only are these two valves often missing, which means that both pressurised and manual systems must be turned off just to work on one, but the manual pumping arrangement is frequently omitted. If there is a second tank, it too should have an outlet valve as part of the tank fitting and should be connected to the first before any subdivision to other valves.

For peace of mind in a heavy sea, all pipe fittings should be well secured, preferably with stainless-steel worm-drive clips, and it is worth a thorough check that they are so once a year and again if ever the water consumption increases. Polythene pipes appear to encourage the growth of algae more so than copper and they will need cleaning for the beginning of each season and whenever

small floating pieces of 'gunge' appear in the water. The easiest way is to make a sterilising solution with a denture cleaning powder and fill each pipe. An alternative is to pop a few tablets of similar cleaner into the pipes, assuming, of course, that they are full of water already. Leave the solution for as long as practicable, but certainly for no less than an hour or two before thoroughly flushing the whole system. If the pipes were really dirty, the first water out will have a most obnoxious smell.

Apart from the pumps, which will be discussed shortly, the only other maintenance needed for the water system is, so far as possible, to use only 'good' water.

Pumps

As defined by the principle of operation, pumps fall into three categories: lift, diaphragm and impeller.

Lift Pump

This first type is the most basic and, perhaps as a consequence, is more robust and slightly more reliable than others. The penalty is that it is less efficient. The lift pump is always operated manually and in various guises appears as a heads pump or a bilge pump. That illustrated is not intended to be a

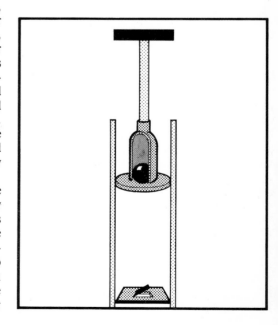

specific pump, but simply a representation of the principle.

When the handle is lifted its valve, shown as a 'ball', closes, allowing water above it to be lifted. Meanwhile, the lower flap valve opens, allowing water to be drawn into the barrel. As the handle is lowered, the flap valve closes and the ball valve opens, allowing the water to pass from the barrel to the space above the ball valve. The sequence is repeated as often as is required.

If one of the valves sticks in either position, the pump fails to work. When this happens, it is nearly always caused by a foreign body lodging itself in the orifice. The answer is relatively simple, entailing the removal of the handle to gain access to both valves.

When used as a bilge pump, it is absolutely imperative to strain the water entering the pump. A piece of gauze over the end of the pipe is not sufficient. A much bigger surface area is needed and this is achieved with a strum box. In shape this can be similar to a funnel and it will have a mesh over the mouth; in addition, it might also have some holes in the sides, though the higher these holes go, the deeper will be the bilge water which cannot be pumped out. It is useful to be able to withdraw the strum box for cleaning and in this respect, the flexibility of polythene pipe is advantageous once again.

The shaft of a lift pump will require lubrication and it is often fitted with a grease cap with this in mind. A turn on the cap occasionally is good practice, but only if the cap itself contains grease.

Diaphragm Pump

This second type is often operated by hand, but can be driven by an electric motor via a cam. The particular pump illustrated is the Henderson Mark V, one of the better and more common versions, though it cannot be driven by motor.

When the diaphragm is drawn out, the inlet valve allows water into the body; when the diaphragm is returned, the inlet valve closes and the outlet valve opens to allow the water to be evacuated from the body.

As with the lift pump, the valves in the diaphragm pump can be fouled by a foreign body, causing the pump to fail. In this case,

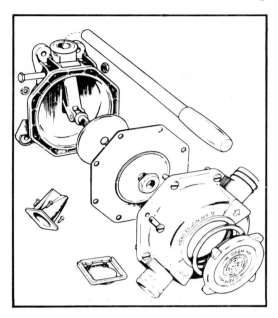

access to the valves is by unscrewing the inspection cap on the body of the pump. A second fault with diaphragm pumps is the failure of the flexible diaphragm itself. If this happens, replacement is the only solution.

Impeller Pump

This last type is more usually driven by either an electric motor or by a mechanical drive

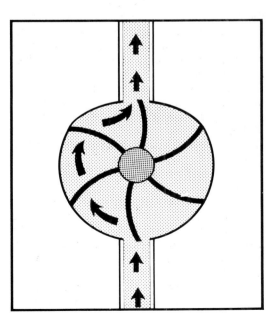

from or in an engine.

The rotating impeller simply 'captures' water at the inlet, carries it around to the outlet, where the reduction in volume between the vanes of the impeller forces the water out.

The most common fault with impeller pumps is the disintegration of the impeller. Of necessity, the impeller revolves at a fairly high speed and the only lubrication it gets is from the water it is pumping. If the water supply expires, so will the impeller shortly afterwards. An exception to that situation is when an engine-driven impeller pump is used for pumping bilges. In this case, there is a bypass feed of a small amount of water to keep the impeller lubricated, allowing the pump to be run indefinitely.

Whichever type of pump is on board and whatever the use to which it is put, it will make good sense to have a kit of spare parts available so that repairs can be effected promptly. The manufacturers make such kits and they are usually available from chandlers.

Finally, do remember to ensure that the water fed to the pumps is free of hard lumps and lengths, such as matches, cherry pips, and the like. This is best achieved by keeping the fresh-water tank clean, a strum box on the bilge pump inlet and a notice in the heads.

12 Ground Tackle and Safety Equipment

Ground Tackle

All the equipment on board a boat which is intended to be used to secure the boat to the bottom is referred to as ground tackle.

Anchors

Anchors themselves require very little maintenance. After some years in regular use an abundance of rust stains on the foredeck might suggest that regalvanising would be beneficial. However, once the anchor has been used a couple of times more, the galvanising will be, once again, less than perfect. Little-used kedges will benefit more from the cost of galvanising than will the bower.

In certain conditions, an anchor can be subjected to enormous strains. If the conditions are sufficiently extreme the anchor can be bent. With most types this might have little effect on its holding power, but that is not necessarily so with a plough type. When lying on a flat surface, the point of a 'perfect' plough anchor will be in contact with the surface. In normal use, it is this point which would dig into the bottom and start the ploughing action which is the source of the anchor's holding power. If the neck of the plough-share has been bent or twisted, the point will not necessarily make contact with the bottom and, consequently, will not start 'ploughing' quite so readily. The result of this sort of twist is that the point will make contact on one side, but not on the other, leading, presumably, to an enhanced ploughing efficiency on one side and a reduced efficiency when on the other. Certainly, the effect observed before the discovery of that fault was the anchor sometimes dragging and sometimes not, neither circumstance conforming to a logical pattern. It required the services of a forge to correct the fault.

The fisherman anchor, so often these days only carried as a kedge, needs a pin to lock it in its assembled position. If it is rarely used, it is worth confirming occasionally that the pin is still attached. When aground on a falling tide, is not the time to be grovelling to the bottom of lockers looking for it.

Cables

The cable used with the anchor will be of either chain or fibre rope. If of chain, it is good practice to even out the wear and corrosion by end-for-ending it each year. If it is in more than a single length, it will be possible to spread the wear even more evenly by interchanging lengths and end-for-ending them. When refastening the bitter end, make sure the fitting is strong enough to stop the boat should it be called upon to do so. Bolts fastened through wood, particularly one with a high acid content, can corrode away, completely unnoticed, to virtually nothing. If the eye bolt or whatever is driven out each year, it can be replaced before its failure leads to a disaster.

With similar circumstances in mind, it would be as well if the line securing the bitter end were strong enough to serve the same sort of load. In this respect, it is necessary that the breaking strain of the line, including a reducing allowance for the type and quality of splices, will be equal to or near the breaking strain of the chain. For example, 25mm terylene would suffice for 10mm chain, and 30mm terylene would do for 12mm chain.

Once each year, all shackles at all the joins in the chain should be dismantled, inspected and, if still serviceable, greased and reassembled. Where 'ordinary' shackles are used, which will be at each end at least, they should be wired for extra security. Before restowing the cable is the appropriate time to remark it for those at the working end, at least, will surely have become illegible.

Fibre rope anchor cable will need a close scrutiny at least once each year to ensure that there are no weak spots. Chafe points can be removed by splicing and serving, and existing eye splices should have the serving removed to allow the splice to be inspected.

Windlasses

Provided they are used regularly, windlasses need very little servicing. Those which have working parts running in a bath of oil will need that level checked occasionally and those with a cone clutch will benefit from an occasional dab of grease on the clutch nut. The best preventative maintenance is to keep them as well protected as possible from the elements by using a cover and running them once each week.

Apprehension in the middle of a dark and stormy, anchor-snubbing night can be minimised by a certain knowledge that the windlass is securely fitted to the foredeck. This knowledge can be kept in date by the withdrawal of the windlass securing bolts for examination each year.

Safety Equipment

Liferaft

A liferaft is a piece of equipment which ought to be treated with great respect. Events have shown that the presence of a liferaft on board is no guarantee of safety, regardless of conditions. But for most of us, it represents an asset which might be useful when all else has failed. For this reason, if no other, it must be serviced each year. Not only that, but it must be serviced by properly equipped and qualified personnel who are authorised to issue inspection certificates.

Once in service, it is the responsibility of the owner to ensure that as little harm as possible will come to it. This means that it must not be used as a seat, convenient as it might appear at times. Those packed in a valise can be damaged by sitting on them by simple compression of the fabric and possibly abrading it against the contents such as the air bottle or tinned water. Those packed in rigid containers are sealed with a foam which will not allow the direct passage of water, but will act like a sponge. The foam will absorb water and when compressed will release it. Unfortunately, it is not fussy about releasing it inside the container or out. So it does both. The water on the outside is usually salt and when this makes contact with the various metal containers inside, the result is fairly predictable. Gas bottles, water containers and torches all suffer.

Apart from refraining from sitting on it, about the only regular maintenance required for the liferaft is to ensure that it is capable of being launched if required. Many are intended to be released by means of a senhouse slip, which after a couple of months out in the elements will not slip as readily as it did at the start of the season. Keeping it free of corrosion and salt deposits will help.

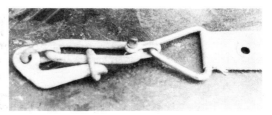

Finally, some skippers like to have the liferaft inflating line attached to the boat permanently and some do not. To whichever group you belong, it is worth checking frequently that a crew member from the other is not trying to impose his will.

Lifejackets

Lifejackets which rely for part, if not all, of the buoyancy on an internal foam should not be used as cushions. The compression of the foam can only have an adverse effect, as can the unnecessary use on the wear of the fabric of the lifejacket itself.

Since they might be needed with the minimum of notice, it is as well if each lifejacket has its own stowage space. When stowed along with other clothing perhaps, it is inevitable that it finds its way to the bottom with the equally inevitable inaccessibility.

It is as damaging, but for different reasons, to hang lifejackets on hooks. As the boat rolls, the lifejacket will swing and, given sufficient time, the swinging will wear away the fabric, not to mention the varnish.

A good stowage is in netting suspended between deck beams, or otherwise to the deckhead, adjacent to each bunk.

An inflatable lifejacket should be inflated orally at frequent intervals if any confidence is to be placed in it. If it stays up overnight, that will probably be as long as you will ever need its use. If it does not, the leak can be found by immersing it in water, taking care to remove all traces of salt by rinsing in fresh water before attempting a repair or further stowing. A leak well away from a valve or a seam can be repaired with the kit supplied. If there is any doubt at all, you must, of course, take the advice of a specialist. Incidentally, the best way of storing lifejackets during long periods of non-sailing is to inflate them at a moderate pressure and suspend by the straps.

Some jackets can be inflated by means of a gas bottle which is attached to the outside. Such bottles have a test weight which will indicate when renewal is necessary. Those with the bottle on the inside should be taken to a specialist for checking.

Safety Harnesses

Safety harnesses tend to be used more frequently than lifejackets and in common with most items on board a boat, those used most are those which trouble least. The occasional application of a small amount of oil to the spring clip will be advantageous, as will constant inspection as they are used for signs of chafe or catspaws in the line. If the line is suspected to be weaker than when new, it needs replacing. That might be after an impact load which stretched it beyond its restitution limit.

All items of safety equipment have a common requirement. If they cannot be relied upon implicitly, they cannot be relied upon at all.

Fire Extinguishers

The bodies of all fire extinguishers must be kept clean and rust free. This will probably mean derusting and painting once each year and then wiping them occasionally with an oily rag. When repainting, take care not to obscure the instructions or to add new ones.

Dry powder extinguishers are quite popular on board because they seem to be able to cope with most types of fire and are also available as relatively small, and consequently cheap, aerosol containers. The larger types will often have a pressure gauge indicating that all is well, or otherwise. The smaller ones have no such gauge and the only check, apart from actual usage, that there is sufficient gas pressure to evacuate the powder is the absence of any obvious fractures of the canister. Even a pin-prick size hole is sufficient to have released the gas, so the most minute inspection is necessary. If there is any sign of rust, there is a good chance that the extinguisher will not work. If the gas is still present, it is still worth giving the canister a shake every week to ensure that the powder has not compacted to a solid mass.

BCF extinguishers can be checked by weight, full details of which will be on the label.

Some extinguishers, such as those produced by Nu-Swift, hold about 2½ gal (12 litres) of water which can be discharged by means of a gas cartridge. By carrying spare cartridges, the normally abundant water can be used for fire-fighting. A similar type of extinguisher can, by the addition of a suitable 'sack', produce foam, which in some circumstances is more useful. With either of these types it is important to ensure that the moving parts move and that the spare cartridges have not become a heap of rust. These, too, can be checked by weight. The foam sacks need particularly careful stowage.

Pyrotechnics

All pyrotechnics must be stamped with an expiry date, after which they should be replaced. They will normally be supplied individually wrapped in a watertight polythene bag to maintain them in the best condition for the expected life span. In the event of the flare itself becoming wet, it will probably be weakened and dangerous to use. At a time when flares are being let off, burning phosphorus appearing through the side of the case rather than its end will be most unwelcome. If there is any sign of the flare having made contact with water it is immediately suspect and will be better rejected. Keeping them in a screw-top watertight polythene container is probably the best way of keeping them dry. Of course some, such as white flares, might need to be available more frequently and will, as a consequence, be more likely to incur damage.

Life-rings

The life-rings themselves will need only cleaning. Any maintenance will be to the lights or supports. If they are of the type associated with lights which switch themselves on when floating in the right attitude, it is a simple check to perform each day. If the lights work, all is well, if not it is possible that the gravity switch has failed, in which case it will need replacing, the batteries have failed necessitating the replacement of them, or it might just be corrosion. This can be ascertained by removing all the batteries and gravity switch and gently clean the terminals with fine glass paper or emery cloth, not forgetting the terminal on the bulb itself. If corrosion was the source of the problem, the light should work when it has been reassembled.

Ensure that the ring can be wrenched free with one movement and that if it is attached to the boat, its line will run free right to the end.

Emergency Steering

If the emergency steering system is rigged, say, once each month, any nuts and bolts or screw caps in the deck will be seen to work. If there is any suggestion of stiffness or difficulty anywhere, effective lubrication can be applied.

First-Aid Kit

All that can be queried about a first-aid kit is that if you were satisfied with the contents when it was made up, have you replaced the items as they were used, so retaining your satisfaction? When checking the contents, remember that the effectiveness of some drugs can diminish with age.

If a new first-aid kit is to be made up, that suggested by the RYA Seamanship Foundation is a very comprehensive starting point.

Dressings

3 triangular bandages
2 large wound dressings BPC No 15
3 medium wound dressings BPC No 13
3 conforming bandages – one each of 4, 3 and 2in (10, 7.5 and 5cm)
1 crêpe bandage 3in (7.5cm)
1 roll of 1in (2.5cm) adhesive waterproof strapping
1 large box of assorted elastic adhesive dressings, individually wrapped
1 eye pad
10 sachets of antiseptic wipes (Mediprep)
1 packet of sterile suture strips (adhesive) (Steristrips)
2 packets each of 5 single sterile gauze swabs 3in (7.5cm)
10 paraffin gauze burn dressings, individually wrapped, 4in (10cm) ('Jelonet')
1 pair of stainless steel scissors – blunt/sharp end
1 pair of spade end tweezers – good quality
10 protected safety pins – 5 large, 5 medium

Medicaments

60g antiseptic cream
35g calamine cream BP
100g kaolin powder
2 × 15 throat pastilles (Tyrocane)
25 soluble aspirin
24 laxative tablets (Senokot)
50g ultra-violet filter cream
5g ultra-violet lip salve

Extra Medicaments for 1–6 year olds
20 Milk of Magnesia tablets
20 junior aspirin tablets
20 Dramamine tablets

Medicaments Available only from a Chemist
24 Kwells or Stugeron (not suitable for under 16 years old) tablets
24 Paracetamol and Codeine tablets (Panadeine Co)
50 antacid tablets (Aludrox)
1 small phial of eye drops (Optone or Murine)

In addition, if the passage is likely to take the crew more than 48 hours away from outside help, the following, which can only be obtained on prescription, should be carried.
20 DF 118 tablets (for severe pain)
30 Lomotil tablets (anti-diarrhoea)
30 Erythromycin 250mg tablets (antibiotics for infection)
Stemetil suppositories (for severe vomiting)
4g Chloromycetin antibiotic eye ointment

Additionally, it is recommended that a foil survival blanket is carried.

Whenever giving medicines to children, take extra special care. Those between 6 and 12 years can be given half of the adult dose; those between 1 and 6 years may be allowed a quarter dose, but they may be advised, in common with pregnant women, to take none at all. For these cases, and for children under one year old, take medical advice.

ST. BUDEAUX

Index

Index